RURAL TELEMEDICINE AND HOMELESSNESS

ASSESSMENTS OF SERVICES

SOCIAL JUSTICE, EQUALITY AND EMPOWERMENT

Additional books in this series can be found on Nova's website
under the Series tab.

Additional E-books in this series can be found on Nova's website
under the E-book tab.

SOCIAL ISSUES, JUSTICE AND STATUS

Additional books in this series can be found on Nova's website
under the Series tab.

Additional E-books in this series can be found on Nova's website
under the E-book tab.

SOCIAL JUSTICE, EQUALITY AND EMPOWERMENT

RURAL TELEMEDICINE AND HOMELESSNESS

ASSESSMENTS OF SERVICES

JAKE F. ANDREWS
AND
ANTHONY I. HARPER
EDITORS

Nova Science Publishers, Inc.

New York

For permission to use material from this book please contact us:
Telephone 631-231-7269; Fax 631-231-8175
Web Site: http://www.novapublishers.com

NOTICE TO THE READER

The Publisher has taken reasonable care in the preparation of this book, but makes no expressed or implied warranty of any kind and assumes no responsibility for any errors or omissions. No liability is assumed for incidental or consequential damages in connection with or arising out of information contained in this book. The Publisher shall not be liable for any special, consequential, or exemplary damages resulting, in whole or in part, from the readers' use of, or reliance upon, this material. Any parts of this book based on government reports are so indicated and copyright is claimed for those parts to the extent applicable to compilations of such works.

Independent verification should be sought for any data, advice or recommendations contained in this book. In addition, no responsibility is assumed by the publisher for any injury and/or damage to persons or property arising from any methods, products, instructions, ideas or otherwise contained in this publication.

This publication is designed to provide accurate and authoritative information with regard to the subject matter covered herein. It is sold with the clear understanding that the Publisher is not engaged in rendering legal or any other professional services. If legal or any other expert assistance is required, the services of a competent person should be sought. FROM A DECLARATION OF PARTICIPANTS JOINTLY ADOPTED BY A COMMITTEE OF THE AMERICAN BAR ASSOCIATION AND A COMMITTEE OF PUBLISHERS.

Additional color graphics may be available in the e-book version of this book.

Library of Congress Cataloging-in-Publication Data

ISBN: 978-1-61942-926-0

Published by Nova Science Publishers, Inc. † New York

CONTENTS

PREFACE

This book provides an overview of the issues of rural healthcare programs and rural homelessness. Telemedicine offers a way to improve health care access for patients in rural areas through remote access, medical diagnosis and patient care; often from specialists in urban areas or university hospitals. Additionally, information about rural homelessness issues including an examination of better collaboration by the departments of Health and Human Services (HHS) and Housing and Urban Development (HUD) are discussed, which could improve delivery of services in rural areas.

Chapter 1- Telemedicine offers a way to improve health care access for patients in rural areas. The Federal Communications Commission's (FCC) Rural Health Care Program, established in 1997, provides discounts on rural health care providers' telecommunications and information services (primary program) and funds broadband infrastructure and services (pilot program). GAO was asked to review (1) how FCC has managed the primary program to meet the needs of rural health care providers, and how well the program has addressed those needs; (2) how FCC's design and implementation of the pilot program affected participants; and (3) FCC's performance goals and measures for both the primary program and the pilot program, and how these goals compare with the key characteristics of successful performance goals and measures. GAO reviewed program documents and data, interviewed program staff and relevant stakeholders, and surveyed all 61 pilot program participants with recent participation in the program.

Chapter 2- The Homeless Emergency Assistance and Rapid Transition to Housing (HEARTH) Act of 2009 directed GAO to conduct a broad study of homelessness in rural areas. In this report, we provide information about rural homelessness issues, based in significant part on our work in rural areas within

six selected states. Specifically, the report addresses the following questions:
(1) What are the characteristics of homelessness in rural areas? (2) What
assistance is available to individuals or families experiencing homelessness
and what amount of funding have the federal departments and agencies
awarded to organizations that assist persons experiencing homelessness in
rural areas? (3) What barriers do persons experiencing homelessness and
homeless service providers encounter when seeking assistance or funding to
provide assistance? To address these issues, GAO reviewed relevant literature,
conducted site visits, and interviewed agency officials.

In: Rural Telemedicine and Homelessness ISBN: 978-1-61942-926-0
Editors: J. Andrews and A. Harper © 2012 Nova Science Publishers, Inc

Chapter 1

TELECOMMUNICATIONS: FCC'S PERFORMANCE MANAGEMENT WEAKNESSES COULD JEOPARDIZE PROPOSED REFORMS OF THE RURAL HEALTH CARE PROGRAM*

The United States Government Accountability Office

WHY GAO DID THIS STUDY

Telemedicine offers a way to improve health care access for patients in rural areas. The Federal Communications Commission's (FCC) Rural Health Care Program, established in 1997, provides discounts on rural health care providers' telecommunications and information services (primary program) and funds broadband infrastructure and services (pilot program). GAO was asked to review (1) how FCC has managed the primary program to meet the needs of rural health care providers, and how well the program has addressed those needs; (2) how FCC's design and implementation of the pilot program affected participants; and (3) FCC's performance goals and measures for both

---

* This is an edited, reformatted and augmented version of The United States Government Accountability Office publication, Report to Congressional Requesters GAO-11-27, dated November 2010.

the primary program and the pilot program, and how these goals compare with the key characteristics of successful performance goals and measures. GAO reviewed program documents and data, interviewed program staff and relevant stakeholders, and surveyed all 61 pilot program participants with recent participation in the program.

WHAT GAO RECOMMENDS

GAO recommends that the FCC Chairman assess rural health care providers' needs, consult with knowledgeable stakeholders, develop performance goals and measures, and develop and execute sound performance evaluation plans. In its comments, FCC did not agree or disagree with the recommendations, but discussed planned and ongoing actions to address them.

WHAT GAO FOUND

FCC has not conducted an assessment of the telecommunications needs of rural health care providers as it has managed the primary Rural Health Care Program, which limits FCC's ability to determine how well the program has addressed those needs. Participation in the primary program has increased, and some rural health care providers report that they are dependent on the support received from the program. For example, a provider in Alaska has used program funds to increase the use of telemedicine, which has reduced patient wait times and travel costs. FCC has been successful in disbursing over 86 percent of all committed funds. However, FCC has disbursed only $327 million in total over the 12 years of the primary program's operation— less than any single year's $400 million funding cap. FCC has frequently stated that the primary program is underutilized and has made a number of changes to the program, including the creation of the pilot program. Currently, FCC is proposing to replace portions of the primary program with a new broadband services program. However, without a needs assessment, FCC cannot determine how well the current program is targeting those needs—and whether the program is, in fact, underutilized—or ensure that a new program will target needs any better.

FCC's poor planning and communication during the design and implementation of the pilot program caused delays and difficulties for pilot program participants. FCC did not consult with the program's administrator, other federal agencies, or relevant stakeholders prior to announcing the program, nor did it request public comment on its design. In addition, FCC called for applications to participate in the pilot program before it fully established pilot program requirements. FCC added additional program requirements after the pilot program began, and survey respondents indicated that program guidance was not provided in an effective manner. Despite these difficulties, most participants were positive about the assistance provided by program officials and reported that the benefits they anticipate receiving from the pilot program outweigh the costs of participating. However, the entire program has been delayed and projects have struggled to meet requirements that were not clearly defined at the beginning of the program.

FCC has not developed specific performance goals for the Rural Health Care Program and has developed ineffective performance measures. The performance measures are limited for a number of reasons, the most important of which is that FCC has set no specific performance goals to which to link them. In addition, FCC has not evaluated the performance of the primary Rural Health Care Program and has no evaluation plan for the pilot program. Without reliable performance information, FCC does not have the data that it needs to make critical policy decisions about the overall Rural Health Care Program. If FCC does not correct these deficits in performance management, it may perpetuate the same performance management weaknesses in its stewardship of the new rural health care programs that it has proposed.

ABBREVIATIONS

APA	Administrative Procedure Act
FCC	Federal Communications Commission
HHS	Department of Health and Human Services
HRSA	Health Resources and Services Administration
IT	information technology
KANA	Kodiak Area Native Association
MOU	memorandum of understanding
NECA	National Exchange Carrier Association
NOI	Notice of Inquiry
NPRM	Notice of Proposed Rulemaking
OMB	Office of Management and Budget
PATS	Packet Tracking System

RFP   request for proposals
SIDS   Simplified Invoice Database System
USAC   Universal Service Administrative Company
USDA   US Department of Agriculture

November 17, 2010

Congressional Requesters

Some of the most promising technologies to arise out of our nation's transition to broadband[1] involve "telemedicine," particularly for patients in rural areas of the country. Telemedicine technologies can allow rural patients to receive, through remote access, medical diagnosis or patient care, often from specialists who are located in urban areas or university hospitals. Increased use of video consultation, remote patient monitoring, and electronic health records[2] enabled by telemedicine technologies hold the promise of improving health care quality, safety, and efficiency. The Federal Communications Commission's (FCC) Rural Health Care Universal Service Support Mechanism—or Rural Health Care Program— was created pursuant to the Telecommunications Act of 1996[3] (1996 Act) and enables rural health care providers to receive (1) telecommunications services[4] at rates comparable to that of their urban counterparts and (2) access to the advanced telecommunications and information services necessary for health care delivery. Access to reasonably priced telecommunications services and Internet access services affords rural health care providers the ability to provide important telemedicine technologies that can improve the care of patients while maximizing limited resources.

Despite these benefits, FCC has stated that its Rural Health Care Program is underutilized, in part, because rural health care providers' needs have shifted away from discounted telecommunications and Internet services, and toward the broadband networks and facilities needed to support advanced telemedicine applications. Thus, in 2006, FCC established a separate pilot program within the Rural Health Care Program to provide funding for broadband infrastructure and services.[5] Also, in March 2010, at the direction of Congress, an FCC task force developed and released a *National Broadband Plan*[6] to provide a road map for attaining universal access to broadband capability. As a result of recommendations in the *National Broadband Plan*, FCC is currently reviewing its design of the Rural Health Care Program and has proposed two new rural health care programs—the Health Broadband

Services Program and the Health Infrastructure Program—in a July 2010 Notice of Proposed Rulemaking (NPRM).[7] FCC sought comment on these and other reforms, which could be implemented by the beginning of the next funding year on July 1, 2011.

In response to your request that we examine the operation of the Rural Health Care Program, this report addresses three main questions:

- How has FCC managed the primary Rural Health Care Program to meet the needs of rural health care providers, and how well has the program addressed those needs?
- How have FCC's design and implementation of the pilot program affected participants?
- What are FCC's performance goals and measures for the Rural Health Care Program, and how do these goals compare with the key characteristics of successful performance goals and measures?

For each of these questions, we reviewed FCC documents, including FCC orders and requests for comment on the Rural Health Care Program, as well as written comments submitted in response to these requests. We also interviewed FCC staff and staff of the Universal Service Administrative Company (USAC)—the not-for-profit corporation that administers the Rural Health Care Program under a memorandum of understanding (MOU) with FCC.8 To provide information on the design, operation, and trends of the primary Rural Health Care Program, we analyzed data from USAC on applications, funding commitments, and disbursements for the first 12 years of the primary Rural Health Care Program (1998 to 2009). On the basis of interviews with USAC officials to understand how these data were handled, stored, and protected, we determined that the data were sufficiently reliable for the purposes specified. To provide information on the pilot program, we conducted a Web-based survey of representatives from all 61 pilot projects that had recent contact information on file with USAC at the time of our survey to obtain their views on program requirements and on how to improve the program, among other things. Our survey response rate was 100 percent. This report does not contain all of the results from the survey; our questionnaire and a more complete tabulation of the results can be viewed in an e-supplement to this report. To provide information about performance goals and measures, we reviewed FCC documentation on the agency's performance goals and measures for the Rural Health Care Program and compared this information with literature on results-oriented management and effective practices for setting performance goals and measures. Additionally, we interviewed officials from other federal agencies, including the Department of Health and Human Services (HHS), the US Department of Agriculture (USDA), and the Department of Commerce, to collect information on FCC's collaboration efforts on the Rural Health Care Program. We also interviewed representatives from telecommunications and rural health care stakeholder organizations to learn about the impact of the program on their members. See appendix I for additional information on our scope and methodology.

We conducted this performance audit from August 2009 to November 2010, in accordance with generally accepted government auditing standards. Those standards require that we plan and perform the audit to obtain sufficient, appropriate evidence to provide a reasonable basis for our findings and conclusions based on our audit objectives. We believe that the evidence obtained provides a reasonable basis for our findings and conclusions based on our audit objectives.

BACKGROUND

A key goal of universal service is to ensure affordable telecommunications services to consumers living in high-cost areas, low-income consumers, eligible schools and libraries, and rural health care providers.[10] Universal service programs are funded by statutorily mandated payments into the Universal Service Fund by companies that provide interstate and international telecommunications services.[11] These payments are deposited into the federal Universal Service Fund, from which disbursements are made for the various federal universal service programs, including the Rural Health Care Program. Companies generally pass their universal service costs along to consumers through a universal service fee on customers' telephone bills.

FCC's current Rural Health Care Program is made up of three components that fund different benefits. As figure 1 illustrates, the first two components— the Telecommunications Fund and the Internet Access Fund—are commonly discussed together as the "primary Rural Health Care Program." Both components in the primary Rural Health Care Program offer discounts on services provided to a single site. In contrast, the third component—the pilot program—encourages health care providers to form comprehensive, multisite, state and regional dedicated health care networks.

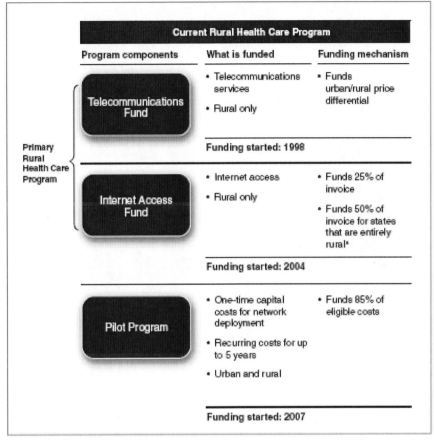

Current Rural Health Care Program		
Program components	What is funded	Funding mechanism
Telecommunications Fund	• Telecommunications services • Rural only	• Funds urban/rural price differential
	Funding started: 1998	
Internet Access Fund	• Internet access • Rural only	• Funds 25% of invoice • Funds 50% of invoice for states that are entirely rural[a]
	Funding started: 2004	
Pilot Program	• One-time capital costs for network deployment • Recurring costs for up to 5 years • Urban and rural	• Funds 85% of eligible costs
	Funding started: 2007	

Primary Rural Health Care Program {

Source: GAO analysis of FCC and USAC information.

[a]USAC has identified only American Samoa, the US Virgin Islands, the Commonwealth of the Northern Mariana Islands, and Guam as entirely rural under the program's definition of the term.

Figure 1. Components of the Current Rural Health Care Program.

Figure 2 shows how the components in the current Rural Health Care Program may change if FCC adopts the proposed reforms described in its July 2010 NPRM.[12]

As the figure illustrates, the Health Broadband Services Program would replace the Internet Access Fund (and raise the discount percentage). A new Health Infrastructure Program would make available up to $100 million per year to support up to 85 percent of the construction costs of new regional or statewide networks for health care providers in areas of the country where broadband is unavailable or insufficient. This $100 million would be part of the overall $400 million annual spending cap that covers the Rural Health Care Program as a whole and that FCC established in 1997.[13]

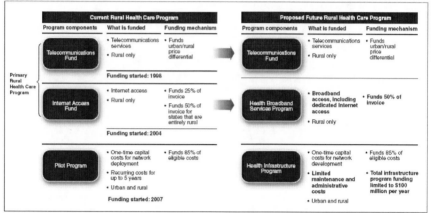

Source: GAO analysis of FCC and USAC information
Note: The bolded text in the Health Broadband Services Program and Health Infrastructure Program components of the proposed Rural Health Care Program indicates differences from the current Rural Health Care Program.

Figure 2. Current Rural Health Care Program and Proposed Rural Health Care Program, as of November 2010.

In managing the program, FCC oversees USAC[14]—the not-for-profit corporation that administers the program. USAC uses its subcontractor, Solix, Inc.,[15] to carry out certain key aspects of the program, such as reviewing and processing funding applications. An MOU between FCC and USAC as well as FCC orders and rules set forth the roles and responsibilities of FCC and USAC in the management, oversight, and administration of the Rural Health Care Program.[16] (See the sidebar on this page for examples of benefits provided by the Rural Health Care Program.)

To be eligible to participate in the primary Rural Health Care Program, applicants must be located in a rural area and be a public or not-for-profit health care provider as defined by statute and FCC rules.[17] As shown in figure 1, the primary Rural Health Care Program provides two types of subsidies to eligible rural health care providers. First, the Telecommunications Fund subsidizes the rates paid by rural health care providers for telecommunications services, such as basic telephone or satellite service charges, so that rural and urban prices are comparable within each state.[18] Second, to support advanced telecommunications and information services, the Internet Access Fund offers most rural health care providers a 25 percent flat discount on monthly Internet access charges.[19] Eligible rural health care providers can apply for support from both the Telecommunications Fund and the Internet Access Fund. However, FCC has stated that rural health care providers have not participated at the rate it had expected.

The steps that applicants must carry out to obtain support from one or both components of the primary Rural Health Care Program are illustrated in figure 3.

Benefits of the Primary Rural Health Care Program

USAC has reported that health care providers are using the funds from the primary Rural Health Care Program to deliver health care to America's rural communities more quickly and proficiently—and with real cost savings. According to USAC, by helping health care providers pay for telecommunications and Internet services, the primary Rural Health Care Program may reduce expenses and travel time for consumers, decrease medical errors, enable health care providers to quickly share critical patient-care information in electronic format, and allow rural health care providers to connect to specialists in urban areas.

Impact of the Primary Rural Health Care Program: Kodiak, Alaska

USAC has highlighted the impact of the Rural Health Care Program on the Kodiak Area Native Association (KANA). KANA is a nonprofit corporation that provides health and social services for the Alaska Natives of the Koniag region.

According to the Information Systems Manager of KANA, the support received from the primary Rural Health Care Program has "revolutionized telehealth services" at KANA. KANA patients once had to wait between 6 and 9 months to see an ear specialist, but telemedicine has reduced patient wait times 2 weeks and has reduced travel costs, since many patient visits can be conducted remotely by other health care providers.

For example, a physician in Anchorage was able to assist a health aide in Kotzebue perform a surgery when severe weather made air travel impossible. The Information Systems Manager reported that without support from the primary Rural Health Care Program, KANA would be forced to go back to using dial-up services. Without this support, "it would be difficult to afford even the smallest connection between the villages and KANA."

Source: USAC's 2007 annual report.

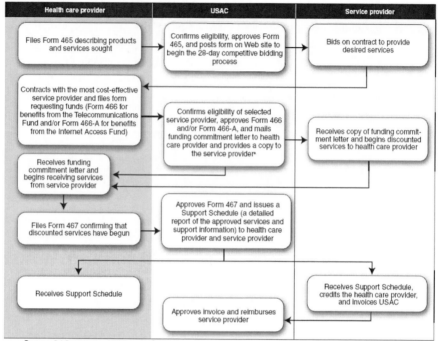

Source: GAO analysis of FCC and USAC information.

^a A funding commitment letter explains that the application has been approved and lists the amount of support the applicant may expect.

Figure 3. The Primary Rural Health Care Program Processes.

FCC created the third component of the current Rural Health Care Program, the pilot program, in September 2006 after acknowledging that the primary Rural Health Care Program was "greatly underutilized."[20] FCC explained that "although there are a number of factors that may explain the underutilization" of the program, it was "apparent that health care providers continue to lack access to the broadband facilities needed to support...advanced telehealth applications."[21] The pilot program funds 85 percent of the costs of deploying dedicated broadband networks connecting rural and urban health care providers, including the cost of designing and installing broadband networks that connect health care providers in a state or region, as well as the costs of advanced telecommunications and information services that ride over that network. This is in contrast to the primary Rural Health Care Program, which provides discounts only on monthly recurring costs for telecommunications services or Internet access to rural health care providers.

Examples of Pilot Projects

Pilot projects vary in their scope, planned activities, and award amount. Listed below are two examples of projects participating in the pilot program and their status as of July 2010.

Palmetto State Providers Network (South Carolina)

This project creates a private, statewide broadband network that links rural caregivers in all 46 counties to the state's academic and large medical centers. Approximately 84 entities are connected to the network, athough more may be added. Ineligible health care entities are permitted to join the network, assuming they pay a fee and the cost of connecting to the network. In addition, the network provides a link to Internet2. The project has indicated it will use the bandwidth provided by the network to support telemedicine, telepsychiatry, high-definition videoconferencing, and participation in a stroke consultation program. *Total award amount: $7,944,950.*

Indiana Telehealth Network

This project seeks to give hospitals access to dedicated Ethernet transport from the individual hospitals to a common point in downtown Indianapolis, where there will be a gateway to the public Internet. The project will build fiber-optic cable directly into the hospitals and will "light" the hospitals with gigabit Ethernet switches. Connection speeds will range from 10 to 100 megabits per second. Approximately 56 eligible health care providers in 41 counties will benefit from the high-speed broadband connections. *Total award amount: $16,138,270.*

The pilot program also provides funding for the cost of connecting state or regional networks to Internet2 or National LambdaRail[22]—two national networks that connect government research institutions as well as academic, public, and private health care institutions—and the costs of connecting to the public Internet. Any eligible public and nonprofit health care provider— whether located in an urban or a rural area—was eligible to apply for funding when the pilot program was announced. However, the program rules required that applicants' proposed networks include at least a *de minimis* number of public and nonprofit health care providers that serve rural areas.

FCC received 81 applications from projects seeking to participate in the pilot program. In November 2007, FCC announced that it had accepted 69 of the 81 projects into the program and capped total funding for all of the pilot projects at roughly $418 million over 3 years.[23] Since then, a few projects have merged and 1 project has withdrawn from the program. The size and scope of the remaining projects vary widely.[24] For example, the Illinois Rural HealthNet project is using pilot program funds to pay for the installation of approximately 1,250 miles of buried fiber. The purpose of this fiber is to create the backbone of a network that will connect rural critical access hospitals, health clinics, and community mental health centers to specialists throughout the state and nation. In contrast, a project in Wisconsin is planning to use the pilot program funds to link two existing fiber systems to establish connections between four hospitals that allow health care specialists to transmit images between facilities. (See the sidebar on this page for other examples of pilot projects.)

USAC administers the pilot program pursuant to FCC's rules. Each pilot project must designate a project coordinator and associate project coordinator, who manage the administrative aspects of the program for the project and submit the required forms.

USAC provides each project with a "coach"—that is, a designated Solix staff person who works closely with a pilot project to assist the project through the program's administrative requirements and processes.[25] With some exceptions, the pilot program forms and administrative processes are the same as those previously described in the primary Rural Health Care Program. However, pilot participants pay 15 percent of eligible costs (and all ineligible costs), and the pilot program funds up to 85 percent of eligible costs. In addition, pilot participants must meet additional requirements before they can receive funding:

- The lead entity in charge of the pilot project must obtain a letter of agency from every entity participating in its project. This letter authorizes the lead entity to act on the other entity's behalf in all matters related to the pilot program.
- Pilot participants must develop a sustainability plan describing how the project will be self-sustaining in the future, to include network ownership and membership arrangements, and describing sources of future support.
- Pilot participants are required to submit quarterly progress reports describing the status of their project.

In February 2010, FCC's Wireline Competition Bureau extended by 1 year, to June 30, 2011, the deadline for participants in the pilot program to submit to USAC requests for funding commitments.[26]

FCC Has Not Performed the Analysis Necessary to Ensure That the Primary Rural Health Care Program Meets the Needs of Rural Health Care Providers

Participation in the Program, Although Increasing, Has Not Met FCC Projections and over Half of All Program Funds Are Used in Alaska

Annual disbursements from the primary Rural Health Care Program have increased from 1998 through 2009, yet they have never approached FCC's original projections for participation. Figure 4 shows the total amount of funds that have been disbursed for the primary Rural Health Care Program from 1998 to 2009.

USAC disbursed just over $327 million for the primary program from 1998 through 2009. Thus, as figure 4 illustrates, total program expenditures in 12 years of disbursements have not yet reached the single year funding cap of $400 million. Also, as of September 2010, USAC has disbursed just over $26 million for the pilot program.[27] Therefore, USAC has disbursed less than $400 million for all three components of the Rural Health Care Program since the program began in 1998. (FCC does not collect $400 million each year from telecommunications carriers for this program, but rather bases collections only on projected expenditures. FCC uses a quarterly evaluation of health care provider demand to assess how much telecommunications companies must contribute to the Universal ServiceFund each quarter. This means that if FCC's proposed reforms create more participation in the program, telecommunications companies would need to pay more in Universal Service Fund contributions. Telecommunications companies would likely pass these costs on to consumers through higher universal service fees in consumers' telephone bills.)

According to USAC data, primary Rural Health Care Program funding was disbursed to all of the types of rural health care providers designated by statute as eligible to participate in the program.

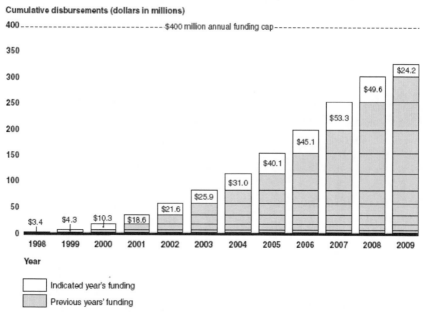

Source: GAO analysis of USAC data.

Note: This figure represents the amount of disbursements through July 31, 2010. Because of the application process, funding commitments and disbursements may be made after a program year ends. Funding for 2008 and 2009 appear smaller than the previous years because a number of commitments have not yet been invoiced and disbursed as of this date.

Figure 4. Cumulative Primary Rural Health Care Program Disbursements (1998-2009).

As figure 5 illustrates, over 68 percent of total applicants in 2008 were either rural health clinics or not-for-profit hospitals.

As with disbursements, the number of applicants to the primary Rural Health Care Program has generally increased since the program began. Figure 6 shows the number of rural health care providers that have applied to the primary Rural Health Care Program have increased from a low of 1,283 applicants in 1999 to 4,014 in 2009.

Similarly, the number of funding commitments issued to participants in the primary Rural Health Care Program has exhibited a slow, steady increase over time from 799 funding commitments in 1998 to 6,790 in 2008. Figure 7 shows the number of funding commitments by the type of service requested (e.g., telecommunications services or Internet access services[28]).

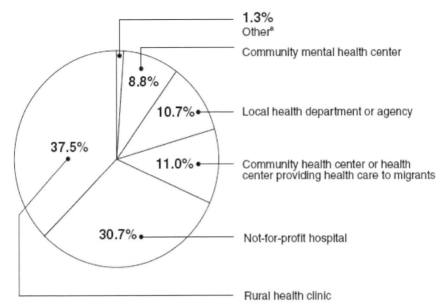

1.3%
Other[a]

Community mental health center

8.8%

10.7% •————— Local health department or agency

37.5%

11.0% •————— Community health center or health
center providing health care to migrants

30.7% •

Not-for-profit hospital

Rural health clinic

Source: GAO analysis of USAC data.
[a]The "other" category indicates postsecondary educational institutions offering health
care instruction, teaching hospitals or medical schools, dedicated emergency
departments of rural for-profit hospitals that participate in Medicare, part-time
eligible entities, and consortia of health care providers consisting of one or more
eligible entities.

Figure 5. Applicants, by Type of Eligible Primary Rural Health Care Program Provider
(2008).

Funding commitments have varied considerably among applicants within
the states and territories, with almost 55 percent of the funding going to
applicants in Alaska.

Disbursements range from over $178 million for Alaska to none for three
states (Connecticut, New Jersey, and Rhode Island). Health care providers in
Wisconsin received the second-largest disbursement, approximately $18.5
million (almost 5.7 percent) of all primary Rural Health Care Program
funding.

For a snapshot of funding to applicants by state and territory, see
appendix II, which contains the numbers of applicants and amounts
committed by state for 2008. Table 1 shows the total amount of money that
has been committed and disbursed to applicants, by state, over the
program's history.

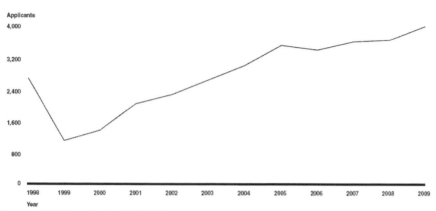

Source: GAO analysis of USAC data.

Note: The number of applicants to the program dropped significantly after the first year of the program. USAC officials said that, in 1998, many applicants started the application process when the program was first launched, but after learning more program details, did not complete the application process. After the first year, fewer applicants started the process without completing it. In addition, USAC officials said that the slight increase in 2005 can be attributed to a temporary FCC provision that provided additional discounts for advanced telecommunications and information services to health care providers in the affected areas of Hurricane Katrina and in areas where evacuees relocated.

Figure 6. Number of Primary Rural Health Care Program Applicants (1998-2009).

Figure 8 shows the total dollar amount disbursed across the United States for funding year 2008, by ZIP code, illustrating the wide variation in geographic use and the heavy concentration of funding in Alaska.

According to FCC and USAC staff, health care providers in Alaska dominate use of the primary Rural Health Care Program because Alaska's rural areas often require expensive satellite telecommunications services. Alaska's vast size, harsh winter weather, and sparse population make fiber networks and other technologies either too expensive or too infeasible. Some wireless technologies also can be challenging, since Alaskan terrain often includes mountains or forests that can obstruct line-of-sighttransmission. As a result, satellite is often the most feasible option for many rural communities in Alaska. Although the cost of telecommunications service in rural areas can vary considerably, satellite service can cost up to $13,000 per month,[29] creating a significant difference in urban and rural rates in parts of Alaska, and making FCC's Rural Health Care Program particularly attractive under such circumstances.

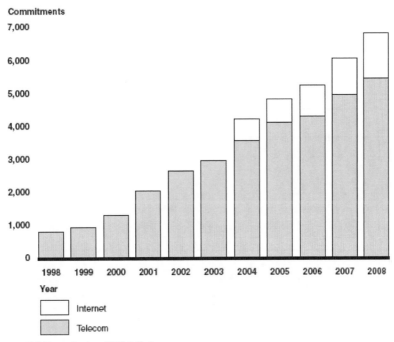

Source: GAO analysis of USAC data.

Note: This figure represents the number of commitments through July 31, 2010. Because of the application process, funding commitments and disbursements may be made after a program year ends. Funding for 2009 was not included in the figure because many commitments still needed processing as of this date. Discounts for Internet access services began in 2004.

Figure 7. Number of Funding Commitments, by Type of Service Requested (1998-2008).

We also found that, according to USAC data, FCC and USAC have been successful in disbursing committed funds in the primary Rural Health Care Program. Table 1 shows that USAC generally disburses most of the funds that are committed to rural health care providers. Of the more than $380 million committed for the program, over $327 million (over 86 percent) has been disbursed, leaving just over $53 million that has been committed but not disbursed since the program began. Some of this $53 million in remaining money will eventually be disbursed as USAC closes more recent funding years.[30]

Table 1. Funds Committed and Disbursed to Applicants, by State and Territory (1998-2009)

State	Committed amount	Disbursed amount
Alabama	$1,244,270	$1,046,086
Alaska	210,847,884	178,341,754
American Samoa	477,999	249,591
Arizona	11,710,540	10,584,443
Arkansas	2,317,205	1,943,684
California	5,426,514	4,599,692
Colorado	1,607,445	1,352,770
Connecticut	0	0
Delaware	825	475
District of Columbia	0	0
Florida	2,558,103	2,200,481
Georgia	6,499,162	5,661,055
Guam	245,612	172,841
Hawaii	2,250,886	2,197,702
Idaho	1,639,419	1,222,038
Illinois	5,267,479	4,611,892
Indiana	2,848,147	2,167,047
Iowa	2,998,147	2,719,887
Kansas	3,541,080	3,371,444
Kentucky	4,178,284	3,868,426
Louisiana	1,056,242	964,264
Maine	325,451	283,445
Maryland	418	418
Massachusetts	504,947	485,983
Michigan	8,395,508	7,240,863
Minnesota	15,000,280	13,471,056
Mississippi	1,281,168	1,203,554
Missouri	2,075,678	1,594,763
Montana	6,143,725	5,743,548
Nebraska	10,692,417	10,137,736
Nevada	631,106	508,815
New Hampshire	94,413	85,158
New Jersey	0	0
New Mexico	3,824,239	2,917,260
New York	487,496	414,847
North Carolina	2,120,879	1,851,398
North Dakota	6,805,852	5,921,101
Ohio	1,887,774	1,636,512
Oklahoma	2,714,135	1,783,742
Oregon	1,103,373	978,239
Pennsylvania	625,395	509,191
Rhode Island	0	0
South Carolina	301,719	265,577
South Dakota	7,281,519	6,632,480

State	Committed amount	Disbursed amount
Tennessee	1,547,336	1,213,735
Texas	4,692,568	4,139,973
US Virgin Islands	718,615	700,027
Utah	4,901,956	4,417,855
Vermont	546,798	498,419
Virginia	4,390,239	3,846,751
Washington	801,684	683,945
West Virginia	1,213,317	1,097,853
Wisconsin	21,304,567	18,520,375
Wyoming	1,283,544	1,206,401
Total	$380,413,359	$327,266,593

Source: GAO analysis of USAC data.

Note: This table represents the amount of commitments and disbursements through July 31, 2010, for funding years 1998 through 2009. US territories that have never received commitments or disbursements are not included in the table. Funds are distributed to service providers, not directly to states.

FCC Has Not Assessed the Telecommunications Needs of Rural Health Care Providers to Guide the Evolution of the Rural Health Care Program

A needs assessment is crucial to both the effective design of new programs and the assessment of existing programs.[31] The primary purpose of a needs assessment is to identify needed services that are lacking (in this case, telecommunications services for rural health care providers) relative to some generally accepted standard.

By establishing measures of comparison, program managers can more accurately determine how well their programs are doing in meeting the needs of the targeted population of the program.

We have previously recommended that needs assessments include the following characteristics:

- benchmarks to define when needs have increased or decreased,
- a plan to determine how needs assessment results will be prioritized in supporting resource allocation decisions, and
- integration of information on other resources available to help address the need.[32]

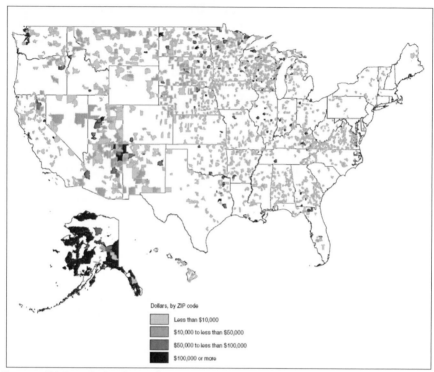

Dollars, by ZIP code

☐ Less than $10,000
▨ $10,000 to less than $50,000
▨ $50,000 to less than $100,000
■ $100,000 or more

Source: GAO analysis of USAC data.

Figure 8. Total Dollar Amount Committed for Funding Year 2008, by ZIP Code.

However, throughout its 12 years of managing the program, FCC has not conducted a comprehensive needs assessment to learn how the program can best target the telecommunications needs of rural health care providers within the broad latitude provided by Congress in the 1996 Act.

When designing the $400 million annual spending cap for the Rural Health Care Program, FCC officials noted the scarcity of information available about the universe of eligible providers, and what it might cost to meet the providers' telecommunications needs.[33] As our analysis showed, the current $400 million spending cap is not based on meaningful estimates of program participation. FCC stated in its 1997 report and order that the Rural Health Care Program spending cap is "based on the maximum amount of service that we have found necessary and on generous estimates of the number of potentially eligible rural health care providers."[34] FCC acknowledged at the time that it expected actual program disbursements to be less than the cap for a number of reasons.[35] Although FCC expected program disbursement to be under $400 million annually, on multiple occasions, FCC has released documents stating that the primary Rural Health Care Program is underutilized.[36] For example, in its 2006 pilot program order, FCC states that the primary Rural Health Care Program "continues to be greatly underutilized and is not fully realizing the benefits intended by the statute and our rules. In 1997, we authorized $400 million per year for funding of this program. Yet, in each of the last 10 years, the program generally has disbursed less than 10 percent of the authorized funds."[37]

When we asked FCC officials what acceptable utilization of the program would mean, they said that they did not know, but that program utilization would include disbursing funds somewhere between 10 percent and 100 percent of the allowable cap. FCC's repeated claim that the program is underutilized, without a more specific vision of what utilization would mean, is troublesome. No needs assessment has been conducted to show that the program is, in fact, underutilized. A comprehensive needs assessment could provide useful information to FCC to help officials envision acceptable program utilization—that is, how many providers actually need services, rather than just how many providers are eligible to participate under program rules.

As part of our review, we interviewed knowledgeable stakeholders to identify potential reasons for FCC's reported underutilization. These reasons include the following:

- Some health care providers lack the infrastructure (e.g., the broadband facilities needed to support telemedicine) to use advanced telecommunications services.
- The application process is too complex and cumbersome to justify participation.
- The 25 percent Internet subsidy is not large enough to encourage participation.
- The difference between urban and rural telecommunications rates is negligible or not significant enough to justify resources toward program participation.[38]
- Rural health care providers do not have enough administrative support to apply to the program annually.
- Some eligible health care providers may not know about the program.

- Statutory restrictions prevent support to certain providers who might benefit from the program (e.g., emergency medical technicians).[39]
- Some health care providers cannot afford expensive telemedicine equipment;[40] therefore, they are not concerned with gaining access to the telecommunications services needed to use that equipment.
- Some Medicare and Medicaid rules, including reimbursement limitations, may inhibit the use of telemedicine technologies; therefore, health care providers may not be concerned with gaining access to the telecommunications services needed to support those technologies.[41]

Despite these and other issues, we were also told that many of the current program participants are dependent on the benefits they receive from the primary Rural Health Care Program.

Although it lacks a needs assessment, FCC has made multiple changes to the primary Rural Health Care Program over time in an attempt to address underutilization and better meet providers' needs. For example:

- In a 2003 report and order, FCC provided support for rural health care providers to obtain a 25 percent discount off the cost of monthly Internet access services. The 2003 report and order states: "Because participation in the rural health care support mechanism has not met the Commission's initial projections, we amend our rules to improve the program, increase participation by rural health care providers, and ensure that the benefits of the program continue to be distributed in a fair and equitable manner."[42]
- In a 2004 report and order, FCC changed the definition of "rural," revised its rules to expand funding for mobile rural health care services, and allowed a 50 percent subsidy (rather than 25 percent) for Internet access services for health care providers in entirely rural states.[43] According to USAC, this report and order increased the number of health care providers eligible to participate in the primary Rural Health Care Program by adding new rural areas while grandfathering health care providers in areas no longer defined as rural.[44]
- In a 2006 order, FCC announced the pilot program, which will be discussed in greater detail in the next section of this report. FCC created the pilot program to address two potential reasons for the primary Rural Health Care Program's possible underutilization: lack of infrastructure and access to dedicated broadband networks.

Without a needs assessment, however, FCC does not have key information regarding the extent to which any of these reasons actually impacted the primary Rural Health Care Program's participation rate.[45] FCC officials told us that the changes FCC has made to the program were based primarily on information gathered through the agency's notice and comment procedures and internal deliberations. FCC officials told us that this is how FCC—as a federal regulatory agency—conducts its business pursuant to the Administrative Procedure Act (APA). [46] However, there is nothing in the APA process that would have precluded FCC from conducting a formal needs assessment. Using data-based assessments to supplement the information gained through FCC's regulatory procedures would enhance FCC's ability to fulfill its role as the manager of the Rural Health Care Program. Specifically, if FCC had obtained data through a formal needs assessment, it may have been able to more accurately ascertain why some rural health care providers are not participating, and have better ensured that programmatic changes achieved the intended results.

To FCC's credit, one of the proposed changes in the 2010 NPRM—that FCC replace the current Internet Access Fund with a new Health Broadband Services Program (as previously shown in fig. 2)—appears to have been based, in part, on a data-based assessment. FCC recommends that the new program subsidize 50 percent of an eligible rural health care provider's recurring monthly costs for any advanced telecommunications and information services that provide point-to-point connectivity, including dedicated broadband access, instead of the current program's 25 percent discount on monthly Internet service.[47] FCC provided us with results from some modeling that the agency conducted using various scenarios to try to ascertain the possible effects of moving to a 50 percent discount level.[48] While the data generated from the modeling will behelpful to FCC in its decision-making process, the information generated was mostly to understand the possible effects on the funding from new participants entering the program or from current participants moving from one funding mechanism to the new program. FCC staff said that they expect the proposed change will increase the use of the program, and that FCC recently sought public comment on the proposed 50 percent discount. A more formal needs assessment, however, would supplement this information and help FCC determine whether the change will address the most critical needs of rural health care providers and whether 50 percent is the most appropriate subsidy.

FCC's POOR PLANNING AND COMMUNICATION DURING THE DESIGN AND IMPLEMENTATION OF THE PILOT PROGRAM CAUSED DELAYS AND DIFFICULTIES

FCC's Limited Collaboration with USAC, Federal Agencies, and Other Knowledgeable Stakeholders Affected Pilot Program Design

To develop the *National Broadband Plan*, an FCC task force recently undertook an initial analysis to quantify some of the broadband needs of rural health care providers. The task force examined the locations of institutions within FCC's geographic definition of rural and concluded that less than 25 percent of the approximately 11,000 eligible institutions are currently participating in the Rural Health Care Program.[49] However, without fully understanding the telecommunications and broadband needs of rural health care providers, FCC may have difficulty in determining why the other 75 percent of eligible institutions are not participating. Moreover, if FCC does not conduct an effective needs assessment, it will not have the information necessary to determine whether the design of the proposed new Health Broadband Services Program will effectively meet providers' needs and will target available funds to the areas of greatest need.

FCC missed multiple opportunities to collaborate with USAC, federal agencies, and other knowledgeable stakeholders when designing the pilot program. These stakeholders all could have provided useful insights into FCC's design of the pilot program.

Such consultations could have helped FCC better identify potential pitfalls in its pilot program design as well as meaningful opportunities to leverage federal resources and ensure that the pilot program targeted rural health care providers' needs in the most efficient way.

Although USAC officials had 9 years' experience working with the rural health care community and administering the primary Rural Health Care Program, FCC did not consult with USAC officials prior to issuing the 2006 order calling for applications to the pilot program. Our prior work has noted the importance of involving stakeholders (including third-party administrators like USAC) when designing, implementing, and evaluating programs.[50] FCC officials stated that they did not consult with USAC because USAC does not formulate policy.

However, USAC's experience with the primary Rural Health Care Program may have provided FCC with valuable insights into how to design a pilot program, particularly regarding the administrative processes and forms. For example, FCC's decision to use the primary program's forms and processes for the pilot program led to a complicated administrative process, particularly since some aspects of the primary Rural Health Care Program's forms and administrative processes were ill-suited to the pilot program. Because FCC used primary program forms rather than creating new and more tailored ones for thepilot program, the forms required complicated attachments.[51]

According to our survey of pilot project representatives, of the 57 respondents[52] that expressed an opinion, 38 respondents rated assembling their request for proposals (RFP)[53] package (Form 465 package) as "very difficult" or "somewhat difficult." In addition, 27 of the 42 respondents that provided an opinion rated assembling their requests for funding (Form 466-A packages) as "very difficult" or "somewhat difficult." Solix officials agreed that pilot participants seemed to have difficulty in completing these forms and attachments.

FCC also missed opportunities to coordinate with other federal agencies when designing the pilot program. We have noted that a lack of collaboration among federal agencies can lead to a patchwork of programs that can waste scarce funds, confuse and frustrate program customers, and limit the overall effectiveness of the federal effort.[54]

A number of federal agencies are involved in telemedicine efforts, and some provide funds to health care providers that could complement FCC's pilot program.

For example, the Health Resources and Services Administration (HRSA), the primary federal agency for improving access to health care services for people who are uninsured, isolated, or medically vulnerable, administers a Telehealth Network Grant Program that provides funds to projects to demonstrate how telehealth programs and networks can improve access to quality health care services in underserved rural and urban communities. However, with USDA being the one exception, FCC did not contact other federal agencies prior to announcing the pilot program in 2006. FCC officials told us that *after* announcing the creation of the pilot program in 2006,[55] they met with representatives from various agencies within HHS[56] in 2007, to discuss coordination.

Representatives from some of these agencies reported that these meetings were primarily informational, with FCC explaining its pilot program to them, and that no strategies for collaboration or follow-up were developed. USDA officials stated that FCC officials met with them prior to announcing the pilot program to discuss USDA's Distance Learning and Telemedicine Program, including how USDA scored applications and evaluated the program.[57]

However, it is unclear how FCC used the information that USDA provided, since similar information was not provided in FCC's call for applications or order selecting pilot projects.

According to federal and other stakeholders, officials at other agencies also could have

- provided FCC with an understanding of rural health care providers' needs, potential information technology (IT) issues, and how to design a more user-friendly program and
- helped FCC identify additional appropriate service providers, one of which had to petition to be included.[58]

FCC also did not request public comment on its proposed design for the pilot program. Although FCC did request comments in 2004 on providing some infrastructure support by funding upgrades to the public switched or backbone networks, FCC did not imply that it was considering a pilot program to fund the creation of private networks, or provide specificdetails on how such a program would operate.[59]

We have previously reported that FCC's use of NPRMs to pose broad questions without providing actual rule text can limit stakeholders' ability to determine either what action FCC is considering or what information would be most helpful to FCC when developing a final rule.[60]

FCC officials said that they did not issue a Notice of Inquiry (NOI) regarding the pilot program because the process would have delayed the pilot program.

However, providing the public with advance notice of proposed changes and an opportunity to comment on them is desirable in that it allows agencies, according to a 2006 resource guide, to "find out earlier rather than later about views and information adverse to the agency's proposal or bearing on its practicality."[61]

Similarly, in comments submitted to FCC, the National Telecommunications Cooperative Association,[62] observed that "interested or affected parties had no opportunity to explore with the Commission various aspects of the Pilot Program."[63] In addition, industry concerns regarding the funding of redundant networks arose after the implementation of the pilot program.[64]

If FCC had provided a more detailed explanation of the proposed pilot program and requested comment prior to establishing the program, it may have been better prepared to address these concerns.[65]

Pilot Participants Have Experienced Delays and Difficulties, in Part, Because FCC Did Not Fully Establish Requirements Prior to Calling for Applications and Did Not Provide Effective Program Guidance

Pilot Participants Have Experienced Delays and Difficulties for Many Reasons

FCC called for applications to participate in the pilot program before it fully established pilot program requirements. This, along with the addition of requirements as the pilot program has progressed, has led to delays and difficulties for pilot participants. Most importantly, the entire pilot program itself has been delayed. Participants may issue multiple RFPs as they progress through various stages of designing and constructing their networks, but the deadline for pilot participants to submit all of their requests for funding (projects submit at least one Form 466-A for each RFP they issue) to USAC was June 30, 2010.

On February 18, 2010, FCC extended this deadline by 1 year, to June 30, 2011.[66] According to USAC data, at the time of the extension, projects had requested 11 percent of the roughly $418 million in total program funding. As of July 31, 2010, projects had requested 17 percent of the total program funding.

As shown in figure 9, as of July 31, 2010, 28 projects (45 percent) have received at least one funding commitment letter, but 18 projects (29 percent) had not yet posted an RFP. According to our survey, delayed and inconsistent guidance led to delays for many pilot projects. In addition, it appears pilot participants have struggled with requirements that were added at the same time that FCC announced the pilot participant selections, such as the need to obtain letters of agency.

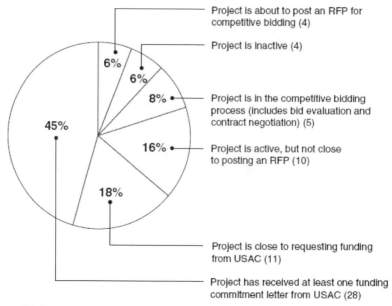

Project is about to post an RFP for competitive bidding (4)

Project is inactive (4)

Project is in the competitive bidding process (includes bid evaluation and contract negotiation) (5)

Project is active, but not close to posting an RFP (10)

Project is close to requesting funding from USAC (11)

Project has received at least one funding commitment letter from USAC (28)

Source: GAO analysis of USAC data.

Note: Percentages do not add to 100 percent due to rounding.

Figure 9. Status of Pilot Projects as of July 31, 2010.

Figure 10 indicates the number of survey respondents reporting whether they experienced certain issues during the course of their project, and the number of respondents that reported they were delayed by that issue. Table 2 reports the results from our survey question that asked pilot participants to rate the ease or difficulty of performing various program tasks.

Four of the tasks rated as "very difficult" or "somewhat difficult" by more than half of the respondents that provided an opinion fall into one of two categories: the task is associated with program processes and forms that were carried over from the primary Rural Health Care Program (Form 465 and Form 466-A), or the task is a requirement FCC added, but that was not mentioned in the initial call for applications (developing a sustainability plan and obtaining letters of agency).

In addition, when asked to list the top three things that program officials should change if FCC established a new, permanent program with goals similar to those of the pilot program, simplifying or improving the administrative process was the most frequently mentioned issue.[67]

Table 2. Requirements Rated "Very Difficult" or "Somewhat Difficult" by More Than Half of Survey Respondents That Provided an Opinion (Listed in Order of Overall Difficulty Rating)

Ease or difficulty of performing various program tasks	Number of respondents rating this task as "very difficult" or "somewhat difficult"	Total number of respondents
Funding ineligible expenses (e.g., administrative costs)	36	51
Assembling the Form 465 package	38	57
Developing a sustainability plan thus far	37	58
Completing the Form 466-A package	27	42
Completing invoices	13	23
Obtaining letters of agency	30	58

Source: GAO analysis of Pilot Participant Survey data.

The Grant Accountability Project, a 2005 Domestic Working Group chaired by the former United States Comptroller General, notes that an agency's ability to ensure that funds are used as intended is impacted when the terms, conditions, and provisions in award agreements are not wellwritten.[68] The group also notes that a thorough assessment of proposed projects can reduce the risk that money may be wasted or projects may not achieve intended results.

FCC's Call for Applications Did Not Include Needed Information about the Eligibility of Entities, Expenses, and How to Meet the Match Requirement

However, FCC did not fully establish the requirements of the pilot program before it requested applications, and it required projects to provide additional information after they were accepted into the program. This led to delays because (1) participants needed additional guidance on how to meet the requirements and (2) Solix staff (under USAC direction) had to retroactively review projects to determine the eligibility of the participating entities and activities.

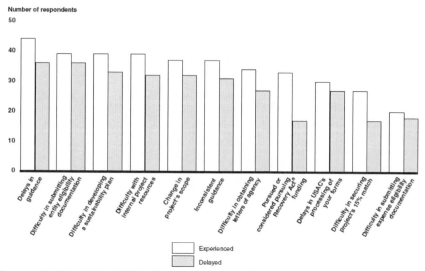

Source: GAO analysis of Pilot Participant Survey data.
[a] American Recovery and Reinvestment Act of 2009, Pub. L. No. 111-5, 123 Stat. 115 (Feb. 17, 2009).

Figure 10. Issues That Delayed Pilot Projects.

In addition, some participants faced difficulties in funding ineligible expenses. In contrast, other federal agencies generally provide extensive detail on program rules when calling for applications for competitivefunding programs, including the criteria by which applications will be judged and how the criteria will be weighted. For example, USDA's 2010 Distance Learning and Telemedicine Program Grant Application Guide provides potential applicants with specific information on eligible uses for the funds, eligible match funding, copies of the forms to be used, and information on the application scoring process.[69]

FCC's 2006 order establishing the pilot program and calling for applications[70] did not provide detailed information on many essential aspects of the program, including

- which entities would be eligible to participate in the program (FCC provided a legal citation, but no actual text);
- which expenses could be paid for with program funds; and
- how projects could fund their 15 percent match.

After issuing its call for applications, FCC did provide some of this information on its Frequently Asked Questions Web page[71] on the pilot program. However, this information may not have reached all interested parties, and it would have been more efficient to determine these issues in advance of requesting applications. FCC also provided some of this information in its 2007 order; however, by this time, FCC was also announcing which projects were selected.[72] FCC did not fully screen applications to determine the extent to which their proposed activities and entities would be eligible for funding. Thus, several of the accepted projects had ineligible components. Specifically, based on survey respondents that provided a substantive answer:[73]

- 25 of 59 respondents included an entity that was determined to be ineligible,
- 25 of 57 respondents included an expense that was determined to be ineligible, and
- 10 of 59 respondents relied on ineligible sources to fund their match.

The lack of established criteria and an in-depth screening prior to announcing pilot project awards led to a lengthy process by which Solix staff (under USAC direction) determine the eligibility of entities postaward. Pilot participants must submit documentation for every entity in their project, which Solix staff then review to determine eligibility. According to our survey, 36 of 60 respondents were delayed by difficulties in compiling and submitting the documentation needed to establish entity eligibility. In addition, although 39 survey respondents rated the current program guidance regarding entity eligibility as "very clear" or "somewhat clear"; some confusion remains, as 20 pilot participants rated the current guidance as "slightly clear" or "not at all clear."[74] FCC's 2007 order also notes that program administration costs, such as personnel, travel, legal, marketing, and training costs, are ineligible for program funding. Pilot participants have indicated in written comments to FCC that they did not anticipate that administrative costs would not be eligible for funding, and some have faced challenges in funding these costs themselves. In our survey, 36 of 51 respondents indicated that funding ineligible costs, including administrative costs, has been "very difficult" or "somewhat difficult." In addition, when asked to list the top three things that program officials should change if FCC established a new, permanent program with goals similar to those of the pilot program, providing funding for administrative costs was the second-most frequently mentioned issue.[75]

FCC Introduced New Requirements after Its Call for Applications and Selection of Pilot Participants

FCC's 2007 order also introduced new requirements that were not mentioned in the 2006 order. For example, while the 2006 order states that the pilot program would use the same forms and administrative processes used in the primary Rural Health Care Program,[76] the 2007 order also requires projects to secure a letter of agency from every entity participating in a project.[77] This letter authorizes the lead project coordinator to act on the signing agency's behalf. Since a number of the selected pilot program participants included providers that were also participating in another participant's proposed network, FCC noted that the letter of agency would demonstrate that the entity has agreed to participate in the network and prevent improper duplicate support for providers participating in multiple networks.[78] Considering that FCC encouraged applicants to create statewide networks, some projects have hundreds of participating entities, creating the need for such projects to secure hundreds of letters of agency. The letter of agency requirement has proven extremely time-consuming and resource-intensive for some projects. According to our survey, 34 of 60 respondents faced difficulties in securing letters of agency, and 27 of these respondents were delayed because of these difficulties. (See fig. 10.)

Similarly, according to our survey results, FCC has not provided sufficient guidance to pilot projects on how to meet FCC's requirement that projects comply with HHS health IT initiatives. In response to a letter from HHS, FCC outlined a number of requirements in its 2007 selection order that pilot program participants should meet to ensure that their pilot projects were consistent with HHS health IT initiatives.[79] FCC officials stated that the explanation of the requirements in its 2007 selection order, in addition to a guidance document created in 2008, provided guidance for the pilot projects in how to meet these requirements. However, one HHS official described the language in the 2007 selection order as vague and in need of an update. In addition, the 2008 guidance document has not been revised to reflect new developments in interoperability specifications and certification programs. Currently, pilot participants are required to explain in each quarterly report how they are complying with the HHS health IT requirement. However, 34 of 47 survey respondents who provided an opinion stated the guidance provided on how to meet these requirements was "slightly sufficient" or "not at all sufficient."[80]

Following the release of the 2007 order, FCC created additional requirements as the program progressed and did not provide program guidance in a timely manner on how to meet these requirements. For example, FCC stated in its 2007 award order that selected pilot participants generally "provided sufficient evidence that their proposed networks will be self-sustaining by the completion of the pilot program."[81] However, program officials began requiring more detailed sustainability plans in the fall of 2008, after some projects had gone through the competitive bidding process and had requested funding commitment letters from USAC. Outside of an October 24, 2008, letter to USAC in which FCC noted that participants should "disclose all sources or potential sources of revenue that relate to the network" and intentions to sell or lease excess capacity[82] in the project's sustainability plan,[83] FCC did not provide any other written guidance on what specific information should be included in participant's sustainability plans until April 2009. At that time, FCC posted an item to its Frequently Asked Questions Web page that suggested more information to be included in a participant's sustainability plan, including status of obtaining the match, projected sustainability period, network membership agreements, ownership structure, sources of future support, and management structure. USAC and Solix officials noted that some pilot participants believed that because their application was accepted by FCC, they met all of the program requirements for sustainability. In some cases, this misunderstanding led to confusion and disagreements between the pilot participants and program officials regarding the need for additional information and the amount of time that a sustainability plan should cover. Moreover, it appears some confusion remains. When asked to rate their satisfaction with any guidance they received thus far on how to develop a sustainability plan, 21 of the 60 survey respondents that provided an opinion were "very dissatisfied" or "somewhat dissatisfied."84 In addition, 39 of 59 survey respondents faced difficulties in developing a sustainability plan; 33 of these respondents stated that difficulties in developing a sustainability plan have delayed their projects. (See fig. 10.)

Program Guidance Is Not Provided in an Effective Manner

In addition, because FCC is responsible for all policy decisions regarding the pilot program, unique or difficult situations are typically referred from USAC to FCC for its decision. The need for such consultations is compounded by an absence of formal written guidance for USAC and pilot participants. We have reported that information should be recorded and communicated to management and others who need it in a form and within a time frame that enables them to carry out their responsibilities.[85]

FCC staff stated that, in some cases, they have not provided written guidance because they want the pilot program to remain flexible. However, in some cases, it has taken several months for FCC to make a decision or provide guidance on issues.[86] However, it appears that pilot participants are dissatisfied with certain elements of program guidance.

As noted in figure 11, of the 59 respondents that provided an opinion, 32 respondents were "very dissatisfied" or "somewhat dissatisfied" with the clarity of program guidance, and 28 respondents were "very dissatisfied" or "somewhat dissatisfied" with the amount of formal written guidance. In addition, as we note in figure 10, 37 of 60 respondents stated that they had received inconsistent guidance.

Similarly, when asked to list the top three things that program officials should change if FCC established a new, permanent program with goals similar to those of the pilot program, providing more guidance and templates was the third-most frequently mentioned issue.[87]

In addition, although FCC recognized in its 2006 order calling for applications that ineligible entities may be participating in the networks and would need to pay their fair share of costs, FCC chose not to establish detailed guidance on how to address such issues prior to establishing the program. Instead, FCC provided guidance as questions arose from USAC (USAC's first request about how to determine fair share was in June 2007 when it was noted that a substantial number of ineligible entities were included in applications submitted to FCC) and from pilot program participants.[88]

According to USAC officials, questions concerning payment of fair share or incremental costs for excess capacity shared with ineligible entities occurred at the pilot program training in February 2008 and continued from participants to USAC and from USAC to FCC throughout 2008. The most recent FCC guidance was a March 2009 matrix outlining nine scenarios in which excess capacity could be used. However, issues regarding excess capacity remain.

FCC's July 2010 NPRM notes that "rules governing the sharing of this subsidized infrastructure are necessary to prevent waste, fraud and abuse," and requested comment on a number of detailed questions regarding the sharing of excess capacity with ineligible entities, different methods for allocating costs among entities, providing excess capacity for community use, and what types of guidance are needed.[89] According to our survey, 21 of 60 respondents indicated that their project "definitely" or "probably" will include excess capacity.

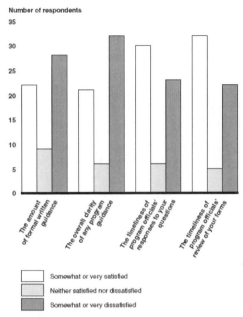

Source: GAO analysis of Pilot Participant Survey data.

Figure 11. Survey Respondents' Satisfaction with Program Communications.

Participants Reported That the Benefits Afforded by the Pilot Program Are Worth the Costs of Participating, and They Were Generally Positive about Program Officials

Although there have been some challenges, many pilot participants emphasized the importance of the pilot program in their responses to our survey as well as in comments submitted to FCC. According to our survey, if pilot participants are able to accomplish their pilot project goals:

- 55 of 57 respondents indicated their project "definitely" or "probably" will have entities that obtain telecommunications or Internet services that would otherwise be unaffordable;
- 48 of 55 respondents indicated their project "definitely" or "probably" will have entities obtain telecommunications or Internet services that would otherwise be unobtainable due to lack of infrastructure; and

- 58 of 59 respondents indicated that their project "definitely" or "probably" will have entities upgrade an existing telecommunications or Internet service.

In addition, when asked to consider their current understanding of the costs and administrative requirements of participating in the pilot program, 52 of 57 respondents reported that the pilot program's benefits will outweigh the costs of participating in the program.

Pilot participants were also generally positive about the usefulness of program officials, in particular their coach. When asked to list the top three things that program officials did well in their administration of the program, respondents provided positive opinions about their communications with program officials, the effort put forth by program officials, and the coaches or the coaching concept.[90] These responses are consistent with those provided to another question that rated program officials—be they FCC, USAC, or a project coach—as the most useful resource for pilot participants. (See fig. 12.)

Pilot participants were also satisfied with their coaches as a source of information. USAC appointed coaches to serve as a project's direct point of contact with program officials.

Of the 61 respondents who provided an opinion, some specifically noted their satisfaction with the ease with which they could contact their coach (53 respondents were "very satisfied" or "somewhat satisfied") and the level of interaction with their coach (49 respondents were "very satisfied" or "somewhat satisfied").

Coaches were rated somewhat lower on their knowledge of the program (40 respondents were "very satisfied" or "somewhat satisfied"), although this lower rating may be related to the lack of established guidance at the beginning of the program and the need to refer difficult issues to Solix management, USAC, and FCC, depending on the complexity of the issue.

FCC Is Seeking More Input and Providing More Detail on Its Proposed New Program, but It Is Not Clear Whether Planning and Communication Have Been Fully Addressed

In its July 2010 NPRM, FCC proposed a new Health Infrastructure Program that would make available up to $100 million per year to support up to 85 percent of the construction costs of new regional or statewide networks for health care providers in areas of the country where broadband is unavailable or insufficient.[91]

In this NPRM, FCC made improvements over previous NPRMs by outlining potential program requirements and requesting comment on the proposed new program.

FCC provided much more information than it did when announcing the pilot program and is allowing for stakeholder input into the program's design. In addition, FCC recognized some of the challenges mentioned in this report and requested comment on potential improvements. In particular, FCC proposed and requested comment on

- requiring that applicants prove or otherwise certify that broadband at minimum connectivity speeds is unavailable or insufficient to meet their health care needs when applying to the program;
- requiring applicants to submit letters of agency as part of their application, rather than after they are accepted into the program;
- having USAC review entity eligibility;
- providing limited funding for administrative costs;
- expanding entity eligibility to include off-site administrative offices, off-site data centers, nonprofit skilled nursing facilities, and nonprofit renal dialysis facilities; and
- providing additional guidance regarding the funding and permitted uses of excess capacity and the allocation of related costs.

However, it remains unclear the extent to which FCC is coordinating with USAC in preparing for this program. The NPRM indicates that USAC will develop a user-friendly Web-based application for participants to use. However, during our conversations with USAC, officials noted that it would take a considerable amount of time and effort to properly develop such systems.

FCC indicates in its NPRM that the new programs could be implemented by funding year 2011. If FCC does not better plan the details of the new program before it calls for applications, participants in the Health Infrastructure Program may experience the same delay and difficulties as participants have experienced in the pilot program.

We have previously reported that results-oriented organizations commonly perform a number of key practices to effectively manage program performance.[92]

FCC HAS NOT FOLLOWED KEY PERFORMANCE MANAGEMENT PRACTICES, THUS IT LACKS THE PERFORMANCE DATA TO MAKE EFFECTIVE POLICY DECISIONS AND IMPLEMENT PROGRAM REFORMS

FCC Has Attempted to Develop Performance Goals and Measures for the Rural Health Care Program, but They Are Ineffective for Managing Program Performance

In particular, results-oriented organizations implement two key practices, among others, to lay a strong foundation for successful program management.

First, these organizations set performance goals to clearly define desired outcomes. Second, these organizations develop performance measures that are clearly linked to the program goals. However, FCC has reversed these two key practices.

In 2006, 8 years after FCC first implemented the primary Rural Health Care Program, the Office of Management and Budget (OMB) assessed FCC's Rural Health Care Program and concluded that the program had no performance goals and measures.[93] In 2007, FCC issued a report and order adopting performance measures for the Rural Health Care Program related to USAC's processing of applications, paying invoices, and determining appeals.[94] However, FCC stated that it did not have sufficient data to establish performance goals for the Rural Health Care Program in the report and order.[95]

Instead of specific performance-related goals, the Rural Health Care Program has operated for 12 years under broad overarching goals, including the statutory goal established by Congress in the 1996 Act, which is to ensure that rural health care providers receive telecommunications services at rates comparable for the same services in urban areas.[96]

Furthermore, the performance measures that FCC adopted for the primary Rural Health Care Program and the pilot program in 2007 fall short when compared with the key characteristics of successful performance measures that we have identified in our past work.[97]

Following is a discussion of these characteristics and the extent to which FCC has fulfilled them in developing performance measures:

- *Measures should be tied to goals and demonstrate the degree to which the desired results are achieved.* These program goals should, in turn, be linked to overall agency goals. However, as we have previously discussed, the measures that FCC has adopted are not based on such linkage because no specific performance goals have been established. By establishing performance measures before establishing the specific performance goals that it seeks to achieve through the Rural Health Care Program, FCC may waste valuable time and resources collecting the wrong data. FCC receives the data for these performance measures on a quarterly basis from USAC, but without effective performance goals to guide its data collection, it cannot ensure that the data gained from these performance measures are an effective use of resources.

- Measures should address important aspects of program performance. For each program goal, a few performance measures should be selected that cover key performance dimensions and take different priorities into account. For example, measures should be limited to core program activities because an excess of data could obscure rather than clarify performance issues. Performance measures should also cover key governmentwide priorities, such as timeliness and customer satisfaction. FCC's performance measures appear to address certain key performance dimensions. By selecting just three types of measures—related to USAC's (1) processing of applications, (2) paying invoices, and (3) determining appeals—there are fewer chances of obscuring the most important performance issues. The measures also appear to take into account such priorities as timeliness and customer satisfaction. For example, the 2007 performance measures include requirements to measure the number of current and pending appeals, and the time that it takes to resolve those appeals. However, again, without first setting specific performance goals defining what the programs are specifically intended to accomplish, FCC cannot be sure that it has adopted the most appropriate performance measures.

- Measures should provide useful information for decision making. Performance measures should provide managers with timely, action-oriented information in a format that helps them to make decisions that improve program performance. However, the data collected by these performance measures—such as the number of applications submitted, rejected, and granted—are output, not outcome, oriented.98 The FCC task force that developed the National

Broadband Plan also reported that the performance measures developed for the Rural Health Care Program need to be improved to assess desired program outcomes, such as the impact of the program on patient care.99 The limited nature of the data obtained by current performance measures, combined with the absence of specific performance goals, raises concerns about the effectiveness of these performance measures for programmatic decision making.

- FCC is attempting to improve its performance management by seeking public comment on performance goals and measures for the Rural Health Care Program in its July 2010 NPRM.100 For example, FCC proposed a specific measure of how program support is being used: that is, requiring beneficiaries to annually identify the speed of the connections supported by the program and the type and frequency of the use of telemedicine applications as a result of broadband access. Although this is a positive step, the NPRM does not specify whether this data collection would be linked to specific connection speed goals that participants should obtain with program funds, and it does not propose what the goal should be for type and frequency of the use of telemedicine applications. While this NPRM could lead to better goals and measures for the Rural Health Care Program, FCC has exhibited a pattern of repeatedly seeking comment on goals and measures for the Rural Health Care Program, which indicates that it does not have a clear vision for what it intends the program to accomplish within the broad statutory framework provided by Congress. FCC has sought public comment on performance goals and measures for the program on two previous occasions that did not result in effective performance goals and measures for the program:

- In June 2005, FCC issued a NPRM seeking comment on whether specific performance goals were needed and on ways to establish useful outcome, output, and efficiency measures for each of the universal service programs, including the Rural Health Care Program. FCC officials stated that this NPRM led to the 2007 performance measures that we have previously described.101

- In September 2008, FCC issued a NOI seeking comment on how to more clearly define the goals of the Universal Service Fund programs, including the Rural Health Care Program, and to identify any additional quantifiable performance measures that may be necessary or desirable. FCC officials stated that this NOI led to the July 2010

NPRM, which, again, requests comment on performance goals and measures.[102]

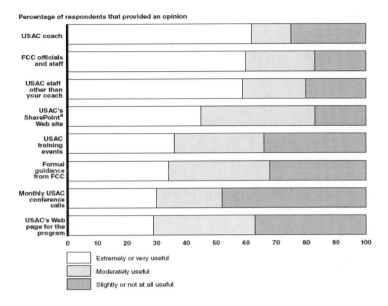

Percentage of respondents that provided an opinion

Source: GAO analysis of Pilot Participant Survey data.

Figure 12. Respondents' Ratings of Pilot Program Resources.

Performance goals and measures are particularly important for the Rural Health Care Program, because they could help FCC to make well-informed decisions about how to address the trends that we have previously described. If FCC does use information from the latest NPRM to develop specific performance goals and measures, it should focus on the results that it expects its programs to achieve.

We have identified the following practices for developing successful performance goals and measures:

- create a set of performance goals and measures that addresses important dimensions of a program's performance and balance competing priorities,
- use intermediate goals and measures to show progress or contribution to intended results,
- include explanatory information on the goals and measures,

- develop performance goals to address mission-critical management problems,
- show baseline and trend data for past performance,
- identify projected target levels of performance for multiyear goals, and
- link the goals of component organizations to departmental strategic goals.[103]

Clearly articulated, outcome-based performance goals and measures are important to help ensure that the Rural Health Care Program meets the guiding principles that Congress has set forth.

Without Effective Performance Goals and Measures, FCC Cannot Reliably Evaluate Program Performance, Which Could Lead to a Repeat of Its Past Management Weaknesses

After implementing the key performance management practices that we have previously discussed—establishing effective performance goals and measures—results-oriented organizations implement a third, key practice: that is, evaluating the performance of their programs.[104] Measuring performance allows these organizations to track progress toward goals and provides managers with the crucial performance data needed to make management decisions. We have previously reported that performance data can have real value only when used to identify the gap between a program's actual performance level and the performance level identified as its goal.[105] Again, without specific performance goals and effective performance measures, FCC cannot identify program performance gaps and is unlikely to conduct evaluations that are useful for formulating policy decisions.

FCC has not formally evaluated the performance of the primary Rural Health Care Program to determine whether it is meeting the needs of rural health care providers, and it may lack the tools to evaluate the pilot program— such as an effective progress reporting mechanism and an evaluation plan. To its credit, FCC has stated that it intends to evaluate the pilot program after its completion. However, it is unclear whether FCC has effective evaluation tools for conducting a pilot program evaluation that will be useful for making policy decisions about the future of the Rural Health Care Program. To track the progress of pilot projects, FCC requires pilot program participants to complete quarterly reports that are filed with FCC and USAC, but it is unclear whether these reports are effective tools for evaluating pilot program performance for the following reasons:

- *Quarterly report data are not quantitative.* Quarterly reports collect data that are mostly qualitative (e.g., a narrative description of a project's network and how the network will be sustained) instead of quantitative. While qualitative data can help officials understand project progress on an individual basis, the information is not objective or easily measured.

- *FCC has not involved key stakeholders.* We have previously reported that stakeholder and customer involvement helps agencies to ensure that efforts and resources are targeted at the highest priorities.[106] However, key stakeholders and pilot participants are not involved in ensuring that quarterly reports are providing the most useful information possible. Pilot program coaches, who guide pilot participants through the program's administrative processes, and USAC officials said that FCC has not told them how the reports will be used to evaluate pilot program progress. USAC and the pilot program coaches work directly with participants and without understanding how these reports will be used, they are unable to effectively guide participants into providing the most useful evaluation information possible. Additionally, of the 45 pilot program survey respondents that provided an opinion, 26 said that they receive too little feedback on their quarterly reports.

- *Quarterly reports may require too much information.* Of the 58 pilot program survey respondents that provided an opinion, 28 said that too much information is required in quarterly reports. As we have previously discussed, an excess of data can obscure rather than clarify performance.

FCC officials told us that they have learned lessons from using these quarterly reports, and that, as part of the 2010 NPRM, FCC requested public comment on a similar reporting requirement for the proposed Health Infrastructure Program.[107]

Furthermore, despite FCC's intentions to evaluate the pilot program, officials have not yet developed an evaluation plan for the pilot program. FCC officials told us that this is because the pilot program is still under way, and that FCC will plan the evaluation when the pilot program is closer to completion (as we previously stated, the deadline for participants in the pilot program to select a vendor and request a funding commitment from USAC is June 30, 2011). However, we have previously reported that when conducting pilot programs, agencies should develop sound evaluation plans before program implementation—as part of the design of the pilot program itself—to increase confidence in results and facilitate decision making about broader application of the pilot program. We have previously identified the following key features of sound evaluation plans:

- well-defined, clear, and measurable objectives;
- measures that are directly linked to specific program objectives;
- criteria or standards for determining program performance;
- clearly articulated methodology and a strategy for comparing results with other efforts;
- a clear plan that details the type and source of data necessary to evaluate the program, methods for data collection, and the timing and frequency of data collection;
- a detailed data-analysis plan to track the program's performance and evaluate its final results; and
- a detailed plan to ensure that data collection, entry, and storage are reliable and error-free.[108]

The lack of a documented evaluation plan for the pilot program increases the likelihood that FCC will not collect appropriate or sufficient data, which limits understanding of pilot program results. Without this understanding, FCC will be limited in its decision making about the pilot program's potential broader application to FCC's proposed future programs.

The *National Broadband Plan* states that for all four universal service fund programs, including the Rural Health Care Program, "there is a lack of adequate data to make critical policy decisions regarding how to better utilize funding to promote universal service objectives."[109] FCC has not effectively followed the three key performance management practices discussed in this report and has not obtained the data that it needs to make critical policy decisions and successfully manage the program. Furthermore, FCC has proposed two new programs under the Rural Health Care Program in its 2010 NPRM (the Health Broadband Services Program and the Health Infrastructure Program), even though the *National Broadband Plan* states that FCC does not have the data to make critical policy decisions on how to better use its funds.[110] In our previous work, we have reported that results-oriented organizations recognize that improvement goals should flow from a fact-based performance analysis.[111] However, the proposed improvements to the Rural Health Care Program are not based on a fact-based performance analysis because the performances of the primary Rural Health Care Program and the pilot program have not been evaluated. FCC officials told us that they believe the proposals set forth in the July 2010 NPRM are "positive first steps" toward creating improvements to performance analysis.

Because FCC has not determined what the primary Rural Health Care Program and the pilot program are specifically intended to accomplish and how well the programs are performing, it remains unclear how FCC will make informed decisions about the new programs described in the July 2010 NPRM. Moreover, as new technologies are developed, measuring the performance and effectiveness of existing programs is important so that decision makers can design future programs to effectively incorporate new technologies, if appropriate. If FCC does not institute better performance management tools— by establishing effective performance goals and measures, and planning and conducting effective program evaluations—FCC's management weaknesses will likely continue to affect the current Rural Health Care Program, and will likely carry forward into the design and operation of proposed Rural Health Care programs.

CONCLUSION

Over the first 12 years of its Rural Health Care Program, FCC has distributed more than $327 million to rural health care providers to assist them in purchasing telecommunications and information services. FCC and USAC have been particularly successful in disbursing committed funds in the primary Rural Health Care Program, and FCC has generally seen slow but steady growth in both the amounts of annual disbursements and the number of annual applicants to the primary program.

However, since the Rural Health Care Program's inception, FCC has not provided the program with a solid performance management foundation. FCC could better inform its decision making and improve its stewardship of the Rural Health Care Program by incorporating effective performance management practices into its regulatory processes. FCC has not conducted a comprehensive needs assessment to determine the needs of rural health care providers, has no specific goals and measures for the program to guide its management decisions, and has not evaluated how well the program is performing. FCC's attempts to improve the program over time, including the 2006 pilot program, have not been informed by a documented, fact-based needs assessment; consultations with knowledgeable stakeholders, including other government agencies; and performance evaluations. Despite FCC's efforts to improve the program, a significant number of eligible rural health care providers currently do not use the primary Rural Health Care Program, and FCC's management of the pilot program has often led to the delays and difficulties reported by pilot participants.

We found that a number of rural health care providers depend on the support they receive from the primary Rural Health Care Program, and that most pilot program participants are seeking services that they believe would have been otherwise unaffordable. It is possible that FCC's proposed changes to the Rural Health Care Program will increase participation by rural health care providers, thus increasing the amount of funding committed by the Rural Health Care Program and, ultimately, increasing the universal service fees paid by consumers on their telephone bills. Changes in FCC's approach to performance management could help ensure that higher telephone bills are justified; that program resources are targeting the needs of rural health care providers; and that the program, in fact, is helping our nation to realize more widespread use of telemedicine technologies.

RECOMMENDATIONS FOR
EXECUTIVE ACTION

To improve its performance management of the Rural Health Care Program, we recommend that the Chairman of the Federal Communications Commission take the following five actions. If FCC does develop any new rural health care programs under the Universal Service Fund—such as the proposed Health Care Broadband Access Fund and the Health Care Broadband Infrastructure Fund—these steps should be taken *before* implementing any new programs or starting any new data collection efforts:

- Conduct an assessment of the current telecommunications needs of rural health care providers.
- Consult with USAC, other federal agencies that serve rural health care providers (or with expertise related to telemedicine), and associations representing rural health care providers to incorporate their

knowledge and experience into improving current and future programs.

- Develop effective goals, and performance measures linked to those goals, for all current and future programs.
- Develop and execute a sound performance evaluation plan for the current programs, and develop sound evaluation plans as part of the design of any new programs before implementation begins.
- For any new program, ensure that FCC's request for applications to the program clearly (1) articulates all criteria for participating in the program and any weighting of that criteria, (2) details the program's rules and procedures, (3) outlines the program's performance goals and measures, and (4) explains how participants' progress will be evaluated.

AGENCY COMMENTS
AND OUR EVALUATION

We provided a draft of this report to the Federal Communications Commission and the Universal Service Administrative Company for their review and comment.

In its written comments, FCC did not specifically agree or disagree with our recommendations but discussed planned and ongoing actions to address them. FCC agreed that it should continue to examine and work to improve the Rural Health Care Program to ensure that the program is effectively and efficiently achieving its statutory goals.

In response to our first recommendation that FCC conduct an assessment of the current needs of rural health care providers, FCC stated that it is gathering information about health care needs, including needs assessments performed by other governmental agencies. FCC also stated that going forward, it is committed to developing benchmarks to define when needs have increased or decreased, applying needs assessment results to resource allocation decisions, and integrating information from other resources available to help address the need. FCC's efforts to obtain information and assessments from other agencies and stakeholders are encouraging.

We continue to believe, however, that FCC would benefit from conducting its own assessment of the telecommunications needs of the rural health care providers eligible under its Rural Health Care Program.

In response to our second recommendation that FCC consult with stakeholders and incorporate their knowledge into improving current and future programs, FCC stated that it is committed to maximizing collaboration efforts with federal and other knowledgeable stakeholders and that it will work closely with USAC to prepare for the new program.

FCC included in its comments an October 2010 statement from the Office of the National Coordinator for Health IT, Department of Health and Human Services, about collaborative efforts with FCC and other federal agencies. In response to our third recommendation that FCC develop effective performance goals and measures, FCC concurred with the need to develop quantifiable performance measures. However, FCC did not specifically state whether it concurred with our recommendation to develop effective goals and to link performance measures to those goals. We continue to believe that FCC should develop program performance goals first, and then develop performance measures and link them to those goals. In response to our fourth recommendation that FCC develop and execute effective performance evaluation plans for the current and future programs, FCC stated that it intends to conduct an evaluation of the pilot program after it is concluded.

While FCC did not address evaluation of the current primary program, it stated that for any future enhancements to the program, it is committed to developing and executing sound performance evaluation plans, including key features that we identified in our report.

In response to our fifth recommendation that FCC identify critical program information, such as criteria for funding, and prioritization rules in its call for applications for any new programs, FCC stated that the July 2010 NPRM[112] discusses these elements in detail. While we appreciate FCC's efforts to better detail proposed programs in its NPRM, we continue to believe that FCC should detail the requirements for participation in the call for applications to any future programs.

In its written comments, USAC stated that it will work with FCC to implement any orders or directives that FCC issues in response to our recommendations. USAC also provided technical comments that we incorporated as appropriate.

Mark L. Goldstein
Director, Physical Infrastructure Issues

List of Requesters

The Honorable Henry A. Waxman
Chairman

The Honorable John D. Dingell
Chairman Emeritus

The Honorable Joe Barton
Ranking Member
Committee on Energy and Commerce
House of Representatives

The Honorable Bart Stupak
Chairman
The Honorable Michael Burgess
Ranking Member
Subcommittee on Oversight and Investigations
Committee on Energy and Commerce
House of Representatives

The Honorable John D. Rockefeller, IV
Chairman
Committee on Commerce, Science, and Transportation
United States Senate

The Honorable Greg Walden
House of Representatives

APPENDIX I. OBJECTIVES, SCOPE, AND METHODOLOGY

Our objectives were to address the following questions: (1) How has the Federal Communications Commission (FCC) managed the primary Rural Health Care Program to meet the needs of rural health care providers, and how well has the program addressed those needs? (2) How have FCC's design and implementation of the pilot program affected participants? and (3) What are

FCC's performance goals and measures for the Rural Health Care Program, and how do these goals compare with the key characteristics of successful performance goals and measures?

Background Research

We conducted the following background research that helped inform all of our reporting objectives.

Specifically, we reviewed:

- prior GAO reports on other Universal Service Fund programs;
- FCC's Universal Service Monitoring Reports on the Rural Health Care Program;
- documentation from FCC and the Universal Service Administrative Company (USAC) on the structure and operation of the Rural Health Care Program and pilot program; and
- FCC documents, including FCC orders and requests for comment on the Universal Service Fund programs, as well as written comments submitted in response to these requests.
- In addition, we interviewed:
- officials from FCC's Office of Managing Director and Wireline Competition Bureau to identify actions undertaken to address previously identified problems and plans to address issues of concern in the programs and
- officials from USAC's Rural Health Care Division and Solix, Inc., to collect information on program operations and USAC's actions to implement prior FCC orders on the primary Rural Health Care Program and pilot program.

ANALYSIS OF PRIMARY RURAL HEALTH CARE PROGRAM DATA

To evaluate how the primary Rural Health Care Program was managed to meet the needs of rural health care providers, we examined trends in the demand for and use of primary Rural Health Care Program funding from data we obtained from USAC's Packet Tracking System (PATS), which is used to keep track of primary Rural Health Care Program applications, and the Simplified Invoice Database System (SIDS), which is used to keep track of program disbursements. When analyzing and reporting on the data, we considered the limitations on how data can be manipulated and retrieved from both the PATS and SIDS databases since these systems were designed to keep track of applications and finances and not to be data retrieval systems. We assessed the reliability of the data by questioning officials about controls on access to the system and data backup procedures. Additionally, we reviewed the data sets provided to us for obvious errors and inconsistencies. On the basis of this assessment, we determined that the data were sufficiently reliable to describe broad trends in the demand for and use of Rural Health Care Program funding. We obtained the following data—including annual and cumulative figures—for funding years 1998 through 2009:

- the number and characteristics of applicants, including their entity type, the type of service requested, and location;
- the dollar amount of funding commitments and disbursements by entity type, type of service requested, and state;
- the number of commitments and disbursements by state; and
- the amount of money committed but not disbursed by entity type and type of service requested.

To provide these data, USAC performed queries on the PATS and SIDS systems and provided the resulting reports to us in July 2010. Data from both systems can change on a daily basis as USAC processes applications for funding and reimbursement, applicants request adjustments to requested or committed amounts, and other actions are taken. As a result, the data we obtained and reported on reflect the program status at the time that USAC produced the data, and thus may be somewhat different if we were to perform the same analyses with data produced at a later date.

INTERVIEWS TO ASSESS HOW WELL THE PRIMARY RURAL HEALTH CARE PROGRAM ADDRESSED HEALTH CARE PROVIDER NEEDS

To assess how well the primary Rural Health Care Program addressed the needs of rural health care providers, we interviewed FCC and USAC officials to determine how the program was designed to address rural health care provider needs. We reviewed relevant documentation, including FCC orders, notices of proposed rulemaking, and FCC's *National Broadband Plan*.[1] We also reviewed comments and reply comments to the record to gain insight into the public perception of how the program was addressing needs. Furthermore, we interviewed representatives from stakeholder groups, including the American Telemedicine Association, the National Organization of State Offices of Rural Health, the National Rural Health Association, the Center for Telehealth and E-Health Law, and the National Telecommunications Cooperative Association, to gain their perspective on the primary Rural Health Care Program.

SURVEY OF PILOT PROGRAM PARTICIPANTS

To obtain information on how FCC's design and implementation of the pilot program affected participants, we conducted a Web-based survey of pilot projects. For a more complete tabulation of the survey results, see the e-supplement to this report.[2] To develop the survey questionnaire, we reviewed comments submitted to FCC by representatives from the pilot projects and other stakeholders in response to FCC requests for feedback on the pilot program. We also interviewed pilot project representatives who were in various stages of the pilot program processes as well as FCC, USAC, Solix, and stakeholder groups knowledgeable about the program and issues of concern to participants.

We designed draft questionnaires in close collaboration with GAO survey specialists. We conducted pretests with four pilot projects that were in various stages of the pilot program processes to help further refine our questions, develop new questions, and clarify any ambiguous portions of the survey. We conducted these pretests in person and by telephone. In addition, we had FCC and USAC review the survey prior to it being sent to the pilot participants.

We sent our survey to all 61 of the pilot projects that had recent contact information on file with USAC, as of June 2, 2010. We excluded the Puerto Rico project because at the time of our survey, it was the only project that had been withdrawn from the program for an extended period of time; thus, although we tried, locating a contact with knowledge of the program was not possible.

Our goal was to obtain responses from individuals with knowledge of and experience with the tasks related to the pilot program—such as preparing forms and responding to information requests—for each sampled entity. Our data set included the name and contact information for each project's project coordinator and associate project coordinator. We asked USAC coaches to identify who they interacted with the most on each project (project coordinator, associate project coordinator, or someone else), and we sent the survey to that individual. If that individual was unable to complete the survey, we asked the other contact (project coordinator, associate project coordinator, or someone else) to complete the survey. One respondent was the primary point of contact for two projects, but a separate survey was completed for each project.

We notified the 61 preidentified contacts on June 2, 2010, by e-mail that the survey was about to begin and updated contact information as needed. We launched our Web-based survey on June 8, 2010, and asked for responses to be submitted by June 18. Log-in information was e-mailed to all participants. We contacted by telephone and e-mailed those who had not completed the questionnaire at multiple points during the data collection period, and we closed the survey on July 2, 2010. All 61 projects submitted a completed questionnaire with usable responses for an overall response rate of 100 percent.

We also followed up with certain projects on the basis of survey responses to gain additional information about plans for using excess capacity, as well as the extent to which the project was impacted by federal coordination with the pilot program.

While all pilot projects were selected for our survey, and, therefore, our data are not subject to sampling errors, the practical difficulties of conducting any survey may introduce nonsampling errors. For example, differences in how a particular question is interpreted, the sources of information available to respondents, or the types of people who do not respond to a question can introduce errors into the survey results.

We included steps in both the data collection and data analysis stages to minimize such nonsampling errors. As we previously indicated, we collaborated with GAO survey specialists to design draft questionnaires, and versions of the questionnaire were pretested with four members of the surveyed population.

In addition, we provided a draft of the questionnaire to FCC and USAC for their review and comment. From these pretests and reviews, we made revisions as necessary to reduce the likelihood of nonresponse and reporting errors on our questions. We examined the survey results and performed computer analyses to identify inconsistencies and other indications of error and addressed such issues, where possible.

A second, independent analyst checked the accuracy of all computer analyses to minimize the likelihood of errors in data processing. In addition, GAO analysts answered respondent questions and resolved difficulties that respondents had in answering our questions. For certain questions that asked respondents to provide a narrative answer, we created content categories that covered more than 90 percent of the narrative responses provided, and asked two analysts to independently code each response into one of the categories. Any discrepancies in the coding of the two analysts were discussed and addressed by the analysts.

INTERVIEWS TO ASSESS FEDERAL COORDINATION

To determine the extent to which FCC coordinated with other federal agencies when designing and implementing the pilot program, we interviewed FCC officials regarding the nature of their coordination with other agencies, and followed up with representatives from other federal agencies, including the Department of Health and Human Services (Agency for Healthcare Research and Quality, Centers for Disease Control and Prevention, Centers for Medicare and Medicaid Services, Health Resources and Services Administration, Indian Health Service, National Library of Medicine, Office of the Assistant Secretary for Preparedness and Response, and Office of the National Coordinator for Health Information Technology); the US Department of Agriculture's Rural Utilities Service; and the Department of Commerce's National Telecommunications and Information Administration. We reviewed relevant documentation and assessed the extent to which FCC coordinated with other agencies against criteria for coordination established in prior GAO reports.

DOCUMENT REVIEW AND INTERVIEWS WITH FCC AND USAC ON PERFORMANCE GOALS AND MEASURES

To determine the performance goals and measures of the Rural Health Care Program and how these measures compare with the key characteristics of successful performance measures, we reviewed the Telecommunications Act of 1996. We then reviewed our past products and science and evaluation literature to identify effective practices for setting performance goals and measures. We compared this information with the program goals and measures that FCC set forth in agency documentation—including FCC orders, notices of proposed rulemaking, strategic plans, and performance and accountability reports. We also reviewed the Office of Management and Budget's Program Assessment Rating Tool 2006 report on the Rural Health Care Program's effectiveness. In addition, we interviewed officials from FCC's Wireline Competition Bureau and Office of Managing Director, and officials from USAC's Rural Health Care Division to obtain their views on plans to implement Rural Health Care Program performance goals and measures.

APPENDIX II. 2008 COMMITMENTS TO APPLICANTS, BY STATE AND TERRITORY

State or territory	Total applicants	Total number of	Total funds
Alabama	139	120	$291,321
Alaska	244	521	35,093,001
American Samoa	1	1	141,191
Arizona	97	148	1,251,742
Arkansas	92	155	616,492
California	130	185	1,026,093
Colorado	35	52	251,697
Connecticut	0	0	0
Delaware	2	2	350
District of Columbia	0	0	0
Florida	22	49	477,243
Georgia	147	431	1,565,191
Guam	2	20	87,800
Hawaii	25	88	148,487
Idaho	59	57	291,740
Illinois	90	190	1,156,549
Indiana	72	158	849,867
Iowa	92	128	557,951
Kansas	82	78	287,033
Kentucky	124	178	499,668
Louisiana	31	36	70,374
Maine	11	12	21,865

Appendix II. (Continued)

State or territory	Total applicants	Total number of commitments	Total funds committed
Maryland	0	0	0
Massachusetts	3	7	151,250
Michigan	156	242	1,537,172
Minnesota	226	498	2,594,358
Mississippi	35	60	178,487
Missouri	81	109	543,686
Montana	83	149	842,040
Nebraska	123	230	1,521,306
Nevada	15	16	91,924
New Hampshire	14	3	14,658
New Jersey	1	0	0
New Mexico	69	98	725,920
New York	31	41	70,059
North Carolina	63	87	315,660
North Dakota	109	146	1,125,118
Ohio	51	57	334,145
Oklahoma	88	63	627,662
Oregon	23	29	300,256
Pennsylvania	18	25	103,740
Rhode Island	0	0	0
South Carolina	12	7	11,453
South Dakota	100	132	1,401,460
Tennessee	53	26	205,404
Texas	78	157	1,038,392
US Virgin Islands	11	11	46,404
Utah	56	109	755,520
Vermont	27	30	108,350
Virginia	152	201	770,336
Washington	47	45	68,045
West Virginia	32	60	213,666
Wisconsin	337	1299	4,940,178
Wyoming	17	30	108,057
Total	3,608	6,576	$65,430,363

Source: GAO analysis of USAC data.

Note: US territories that have never received a commitment or disbursement are not included in this appendix. Funds are committed to service providers, not directly to states. We chose 2008 data instead of 2009 data because many commitments still need to be processed for 2009.

End Notes

[1] The term "broadband" commonly refers to high-speed Internet access. Broadband enables consumers to receive information much faster than a dial-up connection and provides an "always on" connection to the Internet. Consumers can receive a broadband connection through a variety of technologies, such as cable modem, digital subscriber line service, fiber, and satellite.

[2] An electronic health record is an electronic version of a patient's medical history that may include all of the key administrative clinical data relevant to that person's care, including demographics, progress notes, problems, medications, vital signs, past medical history, immunizations, laboratory data, and radiology reports. Under the Health Information Technology for Economic and Clinical Health Act of 2009, beginning in 2011, eligible health care professionals and hospitals can qualify for Medicare and Medicaid incentive payments when they adopt certified electronic health record technology and use it to achieve specified objectives. Conversely, beginning in 2015, the Department of Health and Human Services will reduce payments to eligible health care providers that are not meaningfully using electronic health record technology. Pub. L. No. 111-5, div. A, title XIII, div. B, title IV, 123 Stats. 115, 226, 467 (Feb. 17, 2009).

[3] Telecommunications Act of 1996, Pub. L. No. 104-104, 110 Stat. 56 (1996).

[4] Telecommunications services can include local and long-distance telephone services as well as high-speed data links (such as T1 or T3 lines or frame relay service).

[5] For the purposes of this report, when referencing all programs under the Rural Health Care Universal Service Fund—including both of the discount rate programs and the pilot program—we use the term "Rural Health Care Program." When referencing the components of the Rural Health Care Program that are not part of the pilot program, we use the term "primary Rural Health Care Program."

[6] Federal Communications Commission, Connecting America: The National Broadband Plan (Mar. 16, 2010).

[7] Rural Health Care Support Mechanism, Notice of Proposed Rulemaking, 25 FCC Rcd 9371 (2010).

[8] See the MOU between FCC and USAC (Sept. 9, 2008), http://www.fcc.gov /omd/usac-mou.pdf (last accessed on Oct. 25, 2010).

[9] GAO, Telecommunications: Information on Participation in the Rural Health Care Pilot Program, GAO-11-25SP (Washington, D.C.: Nov. 17, 2010).

[10] In addition to the Rural Health Care Program, the Universal Service Fund supports the High-Cost program, the Schools and Libraries program (commonly known as the E-rate program), and the Low-Income program. Combined, the four programs provided more than $7 billion in support payments in 2009. For more information on other universal service programs, see GAO, Telecommunications: Improved Management Can Enhance FCC Decision Making for the Universal Service Fund Low-Income Program, GAO-11-11 (Washington, D.C.: Oct. 28, 2010); Telecommunications: FCC Should Assess the Design of the E-rate Program's Internal Control Structure, GAO-10-908 (Washington, D.C.: Sept. 29, 2010); Telecommunications: Long-Term Strategic Vision Would Help Ensure Targeting of E-rate Funds to Highest-Priority Uses, GAO-09-253 (Washington, D.C.: Mar. 27, 2009); and Telecommunications: FCC Needs to Improve Performance Management and Strengthen Oversight of the High-Cost Program, GAO-08-633 (Washington, D.C.: June 13, 2008).

[11] 47 USC. § 254(d) and 47 C.F.R. § 54.706.

[12] 25 FCC Rcd 9371 (2010).

[13] Federal-State Joint Board on Universal Service, Report and Order, 12 FCC Rcd 8776, 9093-9161, paras. 608-749 (1997).

[14] FCC oversees the Rural Health Care Program through rule-making proceedings, enforcement actions, audits of participants, and reviews of funding decision appeals from participants.

[15] Solix, Inc., a for-profit company, was established in 2005 as an independent administrative process outsourcing firm—a spin-off of the National Exchange Carrier Association (NECA). USAC is a wholly owned, independent subsidiary of the association. NECA's Board of Directors, by FCC regulation, is prohibited from participating in the functions of USAC. See 47 C.F.R. § 54.703. Under a contract with USAC, Solix reviews and processes applications for funding for the Rural Health Care Program as well as requests for reimbursements from service providers. As a contractor, Solix performs these reviews on the basis of USAC-approved procedures and with USAC oversight.

[16] In September 2008, FCC and USAC signed an updated MOU, which will remain in effect for 4 years.

[17] The Rural Health Care Program uses the statutory definition of "health care provider" established in section 254(h)(7)(B) of the 1996 Act. Specifically, this section defines "health care provider" as "(i) post-secondary educational institutions offering health care instruction, teaching hospitals, and medical schools; (ii) community health centers or health centers providing health care to migrants; (iii) local health departments or agencies; (iv) community mental health centers; (v) not-for-profit hospitals; (vi) rural health clinics; and (vii) consortia of health care providers consisting of one or more entities described in clauses (i) through (vi)." FCC has clarified that dedicated emergency departments of rural for-profit hospitals that participate in Medicare are "public" health care providers and are eligible to receive prorated rural health care support and also clarified that nonprofit entities that function as rural health care providers on a part-time basis are eligible for prorated rural health care support. See Rural Health Care Support Mechanism, Report and Order, Order on Reconsideration, and Further Notice of Proposed Rulemaking, 18 FCC Rcd 24546, 24553-55, paras. 13-16 (2003).

[18] Section 254(h)(1)(A) directs that telecommunications carriers provide telecommunications services that are necessary for the provision of health care services in rural areas at rates that are reasonably comparable to rates in urban areas. See 47 USC. §234(h)(1)(A).

[19] Section 254(h)(2)(A) directs FCC to establish competitively neutral rules to enhance, to the extent technically feasible and economically reasonable, access to advanced telecommunications and information services for public and nonprofit health care providers. See 47 USC. § 254(h)(2)(A). In 2003, FCC established the rural health care Internet Access Fund to provide a flat percentage discount on monthly charges for access to the public Internet for rural health care providers. See 18 FCC Rcd 24546, 24557-62, paras. 22-29 (2003).

[20] Rural Health Care Support Mechanism, Order, 21 FCC Rcd 11111, 11113, para. 8 (2006).

[21] Rural Health Care Support Mechanism, Order, 21 FCC Rcd 11111, 11113, para. 8 (2006).

[22] National LambdaRail was added as an eligible network following a petition from National LambdaRail to FCC. See Rural Health Care Support Mechanism, Order on Reconsideration, 22 FCC Rcd 2555 (2007).

[23] See Rural Health Care Support Mechanism, Order, 22 FCC Rcd 20360 (2007). FCC allocated approximately $139 million annually for 3 funding years, for a total of roughly $418 million for the pilot program. The $139 million per funding year allocation also falls under the $400 million per funding year cap for the entire Rural Health Care Program. Because the primary

Rural Health Care Program was using less than 10 percent of this cap, FCC concluded that the $139 million per year estimate for the pilot program would fall easily under the overall Rural Health Care Program cap. Unused pilot program support can be carried over to the next pilot program funding year. A project can request funding for up to 5 years for its recurring costs. A project has 5 years from the date of its first funding commitment letter to request reimbursement.

[24] At the time of our survey, 61 projects had recent contact information on file with USAC.

[25] Program participants perceive all of their contacts and form submissions to be with USAC. Solix staff refer to themselves as USAC staff when interacting with program participants.

[26] Rural Health Care Support Mechanism, Order, 25 FCC Rcd 1423 (Wireline Competition Bureau: 2010).

[27] As of September 2010, USAC has issued funding commitment letters that total over $83 million for the pilot program.

[28] According to FCC, some services, such as Ethernet, may be categorized as a telecommunications service (eligible for the urban/rural differential support) or an Internet service (eligible for the 25 percent Internet access discount).

[29] I n its 2003 report and order, FCC states that commenters have reported that the monthly cost of Internet access in rural areas ranges from $21.95 to $800 for a digital subscriber line, $45 to $400 for a cable modem, $40 to $300 for wireless service, and $30 to $13,000 for satellite service. See 18 FCC Rcd 24546, ftn 83 (2003).

[30] The most recent year that USAC has completely closed is 2004. USAC officials told us that there are many reasons that it can take several years to completely close a funding year. For example, typically, health care providers pay their telecommunications service bills in full, so vendors have no financial incentive to invoice USAC, simply to pass through a credit to the health care provider. In addition, there is a problem with staff turnover and lack of recordkeeping in the offices of small rural health care providers. Therefore, it is possible that an employee who originally filled out the program application may have left the organization, and the new employee may not know that a credit is due to the health care provider.

[31] Peter H. Rossi, Mark W. Lipsey, and Howard E. Freeman, Evaluation: A Systematic Approach (Thousand Oaks, Calif.: 2004).

[32] GAO, Military Personnel: Actions Needed to Achieve Greater Results from Air Force Family Needs Assessments, GAO-01-80 (Washington, D.C.: Mar. 8, 2001).

[33] Because there was no historical record of what it would cost to provide support to rural health care providers and no list of public and nonprofit health care providers that fit the definition of "health care providers that are located in rural areas," FCC based the funding cap on an estimate of 12,000 eligible rural health care providers on the basis of figures supplied by various federal agencies and national associations. FCC acknowledged that these calculations were subject to error. See 12 FCC Rcd 8776, 9141, para. 706, ftn 1845 (1997).

[34] 12 FCC Rcd 8776, 9141, para. 705 (1997).

[35] FCC expected actual disbursements to be less than the $400 million cap because (1) the maximum bandwidth eligible for funding would not be available in all areas; (2) many rural health care providers would not choose to use the full amount of support; and (3) the practice of rate averaging would result in lower support amounts. See 12 FCC Rcd 8776, 9140-44, paras. 704-708 (1997).

[36] See 21 FCC Rcd 11111, para. 8 (2006); Rural Health Care Support Mechanism, Second Report and Order, Order on Reconsideration, and Further Notice of Proposed Rulemaking, 19 FCC Rcd 24613, para. 41 (2004); 18 FCC Rcd 24546, para. 8 (2003); and Rural Health Care

Support Mechanism, Notice of Proposed Rulemaking, 17 FCC Rcd 7806, 7810-11, para. 10 (2002).

[37] 21 FCC Rcd 11111, para. 8 (2006).

[38] The requirement to ensure that urban and rural telecommunications rates are comparable comes from the 1996 Act. However, if, through a sound needs assessment, FCC determines that there are statutory restrictions that prohibit it from making the Rural Health Care Program more effective, FCC could inform Congress and seek the needed legislative changes.

[39] The 1996 Act limits the type of health care provider eligible for the program. Again, if FCC discovers that statutory restrictions limit its ability to meet the needs of rural health care providers, FCC could notify Congress and seek legislative changes. For example, in the National Broadband Plan, an FCC task force recommended that "Congress should consider providing support for for-profit institutions that serve particularly vulnerable populations." See the National Broadband Plan, p. 200, ch. 10.

[40] Examples of telemedicine equipment include "capture" devices, such as digital and video cameras, radiographs (e.g., X-ray images), and physiologic monitors (e.g., oxygen saturation monitors).

[41] Medicare covers aspects of telemedicine services under certain circumstances, and states are permitted to cover telemedicine to some degree in their Medicaid programs, although decisions to cover these services may vary from state to state. Some stakeholders told us that current restrictions should be relaxed. The National Broadband Plan makes recommendations for reducing regulatory barriers to telemedicine, such as resolving security issues related to prescriptions for certain medications.

[42] 18 FCC Rcd 24546, para. 1 (2003).

[43] FCC stated that it adopted this change because the definition of rural being used by FCC at that time was no longer being updated by Census Bureau data.

[44] See 19 FCC Rcd 24613 (2004). To ease the transition to the new definition, FCC permitted all health care providers that had previously received a funding commitment from USAC to continue to qualify for support under the rural health care support mechanism for the next 3 years under the old definition. In 2008, FCC released an Order on Reconsideration extending the grandfathered period for an additional 3 years. Rural Health Care Support Mechanism, Order on Reconsideration, 23 FCC Rcd 2539, 2541, para. 4. (2008). The Wireline Competition Bureau has recently sought comment on the petition filed by the Nebraska Public Service Commission to permanently grandfather rural health care providers that would not be eligible for universal service support after June 30, 2011, absent FCC action. See Comment Sought on Request to Permanently Grandfather Rural Health Care Providers that Require Funding Commitments Prior to July 1, 2005 So That They Will Remain Eligible for Universal Service, Public Notice, 25 FCC Rcd 10872 (2010).

[45] 21 FCC Rcd 11111 (2006).

[46] Administrative Procedure Act, 5 USC. §§ 551 et seq.

[47] 25 FCC Rcd 9371 (2010).

[48] The model, which is not publicly available, also simulated the effects of a 60 percent discount and a simplified application process.

[49] National Broadband Plan, p. 214, ch. 10.

[50] GAO, Equal Employment Opportunity: Pilot Projects Could Help Test Solutions to Longstanding Concerns with the EEO Complaint Process, GAO-09-712 (Washington, D.C.: Aug. 12, 2009); and Executive Guide: Effectively Implementing the Government Performance and Results Act, GAO/GGD-96-118 (Washington, D.C.: June 1, 1996).

[51] For example, the primary Rural Health Care Program Forms 465 and 466-A are designed for support of eligible costs at one site. However, the pilot program funds eligible costs for pilot projects that can have hundreds of sites, and both eligible and ineligible costs must be allocated among all of the sites in a project. To address this issue, program officials created a Form 465 attachment that requires projects to fill in 48 columns of information for each site in their project. In some cases, this requirement has led to eligibility spreadsheets that are over 100 pages long. Similarly, projects submitting a Form 466-A must also complete an attachment that requires 45 columns of information for each site in a project as well as a 20-column Network Cost Worksheet to allocate costs among each site in a project.

[52] Each respondent represents 1 pilot project. Although we received usable questionnaires from each of the 61 projects, in some cases, not all 61 answered a question, or in some cases, selected options such as "no opinion" or "don't know." Thus, the total number of respondents that provided a substantive answer is noted each time we report a survey result, and may change with each question.

[53] The RFP is the first step toward establishing a contract for services and creating the networks envisioned in the applications submitted to FCC more than 3 years ago.

[54] GAO, Results-Oriented Government: Practices That Can Help Enhance and Sustain Collaboration among Federal Agencies, GAO-06-15 (Washington, D.C.: Oct. 21, 2005).

[55] 21 FCC Rcd 11111 (2006).

[56] According to FCC, the agencies and offices represented included the Agency for Healthcare Research and Quality, the Centers for Disease Control and Prevention, the Centers for Medicare and Medicaid Services, HRSA, the National Library of Medicine, the Office of the Assistant Secretary for Preparedness and Response, and the Office of the National Coordinator for Health Information Technology.

[57] USDA's Distance Learning and Telemedicine Program provides loans and grants to rural community facilities (including hospitals) for advanced telecommunications systems that can provide health care and educational benefits to rural areas.

[58] FCC's initial order only funded connections with Internet2, even though a similar nonprofit entity, National LambdaRail, could provide similar services to pilot participants. Following a petition filed by National LambdaRail, FCC addressed this matter by issuing another order allowing connections with either entity. See 22 FCC Rcd 2555 (2007).

[59] 19 FCC Rcd 24613 (2004).

[60] GAO, FCC Management: Improvements Needed in Communication, Decision-Making Processes, and Workforce Planning, GAO-10-79 (Washington, D.C.: Dec. 17, 2009).

[61] Jeffrey Lubbers, A Guide to Federal Agency Rulemaking, 4th ed. (Chicago: 2006). This is a resource guide created by the Administrative Law and Regulatory Practice and Government and Public Sector Lawyers Division of the American Bar Association.

[62] The National Telecommunications Cooperative Association is an industry association representing rural telecommunications providers.

[63] Comments of the National Telecommunications Cooperative Association in WC Docket No. 02-60 (Public Notice seeking comment on the National LambdaRail, Inc.'s Petition for Reconsideration or, in the alternative, Clarification of FCC's Sept. 29, 2006, Order establishing the Rural Health Care Pilot Program), p. 2 (Nov. 21, 2006).

[64] See, for example, Reply Comments of the Montana Telecommunications Association in WC Docket No. 02-60 (Rural Health Care NPRM, 25 FCC Rcd 9371 (2010) (Sept. 23, 2010); but see Reply Comments of the Health Information Exchange of Montana, Inc., in WC Docket No. 02-60 (Rural Health Care NPRM, 25 FCC Rcd 9371 (2010)), pp. 6-9 (Sept. 23, 2010).

[65] Commissioner Jonathan Adelstein, in his statement to the 2006 order, noted concern with the lack of comments. Specifically, he said the following: "Had we sought comment on whether to create a pilot program and how to tailor it, we likely would have greater clarity and transparency here but, unfortunately, that is not the case." See 21 FCC Rcd 11111, 11121 (2006).

[66] 25 FCC Rcd 1423 (Wireline Competition Bureau: 2010).

[67] This statement is based on our analysis of survey respondents' verbatim responses.

[68] Domestic Working Group, Grant Accountability Project: Guide to Opportunities for Improving Grant Accountability (Washington, D.C.: October 2005).

[69] US Department of Agriculture, Rural Utilities Service, Distance Learning and Telemedicine Program: Grant Application Guide (Washington, D.C.: 2010).

[70] 21 FCC Rcd 11111 (2006).

[71] See the following Web address: http://www.fcc.gov/cgb/rural/rhcp.html#faqs (last accessed on Nov. 9, 2010).

[72] 22 FCC Rcd 20360 (2007).

[73] Excluding respondents that answered "don't know" or did not respond to the question.

[74] Two respondents selected "no opinion."

[75] This statement is based on our analysis of survey respondents' verbatim responses.

[76] 21 FCC Rcd 11111 (2006).

[77] 22 FCC Rcd 20360 (2007).

[78] 22 FCC Rcd 20360, 20406, para. 87 (2007).

[79] "In particular, where feasible, selected participants shall: (1) use health IT systems and products that meet interoperability standards recognized by the HHS Secretary; (2) use health IT products certified by the Certification Commission for Healthcare Information Technology; (3) support the [Nationwide Health Information Network] NHIN architecture by coordinating activities with the organizations performing NHIN trial implementations; (4) use resources available at HHS's [Agency for Healthcare Research and Quality] AHRQ National Resource Center for Health Information Technology; (5) educate themselves concerning the Pandemic and All Hazards Preparedness Act and coordinate with the HHS Assistant Secretary for Public Response [sic] as a resource for telehealth inventory and for the implementation of other preparedness and response initiatives; and (6) use resources available through HHS's [Centers for Disease Control and Prevention] CDC [Public Health Information Network] PHIN to facilitate interoperability with public health and emergency organizations. Finally, selected participants shall coordinate in the use of their health care networks with HHS and, in particular, with CDC in instances of national, regional, or local public health emergencies (e.g., pandemics, bioterrorism). In such instances, where feasible, selected participants shall provide access to their supported networks to HHS, including CDC, and other public health officials." See 22 FCC Rcd 20360, 20402-03, para. 82 (2007).

[80] Two respondents rated the guidance "completely sufficient"; 11 respondents rated the guidance "somewhat sufficient"; and 13 respondents stated they did not know. One respondent did not answer the question.

[81] 22 FCC Rcd 20360, 20388-89, para. 54 (2007).

[82] Generally defined by FCC as installing or having more fiber or similar facilities than is needed by a project's current members.

[83] Federal Communications Commission, letter from Dana Shaffer to Scott Barash, WC 02-60 (Oct. 24, 2008). See the following Web address: http://www.fcc.gov/cgb/rural/wcbletter.pdf (last accessed on Oct. 26, 2010).

[84] Twenty-seven survey respondents were "somewhat satisfied" or "very satisfied" with the guidance; 12 respondents stated they were "neither satisfied nor dissatisfied"; and 1 respondent stated they had not received any guidance.

[85] GAO, Standards for Internal Control in the Federal Government, GAO/AIMD-00-21.3.1 (November 1999).

[86] For example, in September 2009, the Southwest Alabama project appealed USAC's decision that its off-site administrative office was ineligible, arguing that it provided functions that were necessary for the provision of health care services, and citing pilot program order language that recognized a component of an eligible health care provider is eligible when the facility is part of the eligible health care provider, even when the function that the facility performs on its own would not be eligible (emergency medical service facilities). According to USAC, the appeal raised concerns because while the denial was consistent with FCC guidance for the pilot program, it was inconsistent with USAC policy for participants in the primary program. USAC formally requested guidance from FCC in January 2010. According to USAC officials, FCC indicated USAC should deny the appeal and have the project appeal to FCC. FCC officials noted that FCC did not provide written guidance on USAC's letter, since it understood that an appeal would be forthcoming, and the issue would be addressed at that time. USAC denied the appeal in March 2010, and the project appealed to FCC on May 10, 2010. One month later, FCC issued a request for comments on the appeal, with all comments due by July 26, 2010. No comments were filed, and no decision was made as of August 4, 2010. See Comment Sought on Southwest Alabama Community Mental Health Request for Review of Decision by the Universal Service Administrative Company, Public Notice, 25 FCC Rcd 7419 (2010). The National Broadband Plan recommended that FCC expand its interpretation of eligible health care providers to allow participation by off-site administrative offices. See the National Broadband Plan, p. 216 (Rec. 10.8). In addition, as we note later in this report, in its July NPRM, FCC has proposed and sought comment on amending its rules to permit certain offsite administrative offices to have the opportunity to receive rural health care support. See 25 FCC Rcd 9371, 9416-18, pp. 116-119 (2010).

[87] This statement is based on our analysis of survey respondents' verbatim responses.

[88] Due to statutory restrictions, pilot participants cannot sell fiber or facilities paid for with pilot program funds. However, some pilot participants indicated interest in sharing, leasing, and selling excess capacity to other entities, and a number of complicated questions arose. Specifically, section 254(h)(3) provides that "[t]elecommunications services and network capacity provided to a public institutional telecommunications user under this section may not be sold, resold, or otherwise transferred by such user in consideration for money or any other thing of value." See 47 USC. § 254(h)(3). FCC interpreted this section to restrict the resale of any services purchased pursuant to the section 254(h) discount for services under the RHC support mechanism. See 47 C.F.R. § 54.617; see also 12 FCC Rcd 8776, 8795, para. 33 (1997).

[89] 25 FCC Rcd 9371, 9400-9404, paras. 67-82 (2010).

[90] This statement is based on our analysis of survey respondents' verbatim responses.

[91] 25 FCC Rcd 9371 (2010).

[92] GAO/GGD-96-118.

[93] See the following Web address: http://www.whitehouse.gov/omb/expectmore/summary/10003110.2006.html (last accessed on Oct. 27, 2010). OMB's Rural Health Care Program assessment was last updated in January 2009.

[94] See Comprehensive Review of the Universal Service Fund Management, Administration, and Oversight, Report and Order, 22 FCC Rcd 16372 (2007). In the 2007 report and order, FCC stated that the measures would apply only to the primary Rural Health Care Program. However, in the 2008 MOU with USAC, FCC clarified that these measures also apply to the pilot program.

[95] 22 FCC Rcd 16372, 16396, para. 54 (2007).

[96] Section 254(h)(1)(A) provides, "A telecommunications carrier shall, upon receiving a bona fide request, provide telecommunications services which are necessary for the provision of health care services in a State, including instruction relating to such services, to any public or nonprofit health care provider that serves persons who reside in rural areas in that State at rates that are reasonably comparable to rates charged for similar services in urban areas in that State. A telecommunications carrier providing service under this paragraph shall be entitled to have an amount equal to the difference, if any, between the rates for services provided to health care providers for rural areas in a State and the rates for similar services provided to other customers in comparable rural areas in that State treated as a service obligation as a part of its obligation to participate in the mechanisms to preserve and advance universal service." See 47 USC. § 254(h)(1)(A).

[97] See, for example, GAO, Pipeline Safety: Management of the Office of Pipeline Safety's Enforcement Program Needs Further Strengthening, GAO-04-801 (Washington, D.C.: July 23, 2004); Agency Performance Plans: Examples of Practices That Can Improve Usefulness to Decisionmakers, GAO/GGD/AIMD-99-69 (Washington, D.C.: Feb. 26, 1999); and GAO/GGD-96-118. We have also identified specific attributes of successful performance measures linked to these characteristics. See GAO, Tax Administration: IRS Needs to Further Refine Its Tax Filing Season Performance Measures, GAO-03-143 (Washington, D.C.: Nov. 22, 2002).

[98] OMB has noted that performance measures should reflect desired outcomes, which describe the intended results of the program, not simply outputs, which describe the level of activity.

[99] National Broadband Plan, p. 200, ch. 10.

[100] 25 FCC Rcd 9371 (2010).

[101] Comprehensive Review of the Universal Service Fund Management, Administration, and Oversight, Notice of Proposed Rulemaking and Further Notice of Proposed Rulemaking, 20 FCC Rcd. 11308 (2005).

[102] Comprehensive Review of the Universal Service Fund Management, Administration, and Oversight, Notice of Inquiry, 23 FCC Rcd 13583 (2008).

[103] See, for example, GAO-08-633 and GAO/GGD/AIMD-99-69.

[104] GAO/GGD-96-118.

[105] GAO/GGD-96-118.

[106] GAO/GGD-96-118.

[107] 25 FCC Rcd 9371, 9404-05, para. 84 (2010).

[108] GAO, Tax Administration: IRS Needs to Strengthen Its Approach for Evaluating SRFMI Data-Sharing Pilot Program, GAO-09-45 (Washington, D.C.: Nov. 7, 2008); Limitations in DOD's Evaluation Plan for EEO Complaint Pilot Program Hinder Determination of Pilot Results, GAO 08-387R (Washington, D.C.: Feb. 22, 2008); and Equal Employment Opportunity: DOD's EEO Pilot Program Under Way, but Improvements Needed to DOD's Evaluation Plan, GAO-06-538 (Washington, D.C.: May 5, 2006).

[109] National Broadband Plan, p. 144, ch. 8.

[110] 25 FCC Rcd 9371 (2010).

[111] GAO/GGD-96-118.
[112] 25 FCC Rcd 9371 (2010).

End Notes for Appendix I

[1] Federal Communications Commission, Connecting America: The National Broadband Plan (Mar. 16, 2010).
[2] GAO, Telecommunications: Information on Participation in the Rural Health Care Pilot Program, GAO-11-25SP (Washington, D.C.: Nov. 17, 2010).

In: Rural Telemedicine and Homelessness   ISBN: 978-1-61942-926-0
Editors: J. Andrews and A. Harper   © 2012 Nova Science Publishers, Inc

Chapter 2

RURAL HOMELESSNESS: BETTER COLLABORATION BY HHS AND HUD COULD IMPROVE DELIVERY OF SERVICES IN RURAL AREAS*

The United States Government Accountability Office

WHY GAO DID THIS STUDY

The Homeless Emergency Assistance and Rapid Transition to Housing (HEARTH) Act of 2009 directed GAO to conduct a broad study of homelessness in rural areas. In this report, we provide information about rural homelessness issues, based in significant part on our work in rural areas within six selected states. Specifically, the report addresses the following questions: (1) What are the characteristics of homelessness in rural areas? (2) What assistance is available to individuals or families experiencing homelessness and what amount of funding have the federal departments and agencies awarded to organizations that assist persons experiencing homelessness in rural areas? (3) What barriers do persons experiencing homelessness and homeless service providers encounter when seeking assistance or funding to

---

* This is an edited, reformatted and augmented version of The United States Government Accountability Office publication, Report to Congressional Committees GAO-10-724, dated July 2010.

provide assistance? To address these issues, GAO reviewed relevant literature, conducted site visits, and interviewed agency officials.

WHAT GAO RECOMMENDS

GAO recommends that the Departments of Housing and Urban Development (HUD) and Health and Human Services (HHS) explore further opportunities to strengthen formal collaboration on linking housing and supportive services to address homelessness, with specific consideration for how such collaboration can minimize barriers to service provision in rural areas. HHS and HUD generally agreed with the recommendation.

WHAT GAO FOUND

Rural homelessness involves a range of living situations but comparing the extent of homelessness in rural and nonrural areas is difficult primarily due to data limitations. Based on GAO visits to six states, persons experiencing homelessness in rural areas could be living in one of a limited number of shelters, in extremely overcrowded situations, in severely substandard housing, or outdoors. While HUD and other agencies collect some data on homeless populations, several challenges exist in using these data to compare the extent of homelessness in rural and nonrural areas. They include difficulties in counting transient populations, limited reporting by service providers in federal data systems, inconsistent reporting across programs, and focusing on the segments of the homeless population that the agency serves. Definitional differences also make comparisons difficult. For instance, the three most common federal definitions of rural use differing criteria such as population or proximity to urban areas. Even within one measure such as population, different agencies can use different parameters and therefore identify different areas as rural.

A number of federal programs exist to support those experiencing homelessness in rural areas. Targeted and nontargeted programs fund permanent and emergency housing and supportive services such as mental health services, case management, and job training. However, federal agencies maintain limited data on the amount of homeless assistance awarded to rural areas, making comparisons with assistance awarded to nonrural areas difficult.

For instance, HUD maintains some data on the amount of homeless assistance awarded to rural areas through its targeted programs, but the data are based on providers' identification of locations as rural or not. Nontargeted programs can serve persons experiencing homelessness but do not track how much funding is used for homeless assistance. As a result of data limitations such as these, comparisons of funding levels offer limited insight into the relationship between the size of the homeless population in an area and the amount of funding received.

Barriers to accessing and providing homeless services in rural areas include limited access to services, large service areas, dispersed populations, and a lack of transportation and affordable housing according to state and local officials and persons experiencing homelessness in the states we visited. For instance, many rural areas have few shelters or shelters with few beds serving very large areas. A program in which HUD provides housing vouchers to homeless veterans and the Department of Veterans Affairs provides clinical and case management services to these same veterans is one of a limited number of examples of formal collaboration and leveraging of federal resources that link housing and supportive services. The effects of limited collaboration may be particularly acute in rural areas because of the barriers cited above. Without a more formal linking of housing and supportive services by HUD and HHS, two of the key agencies for funding these activities, the effectiveness of federal efforts to address homelessness may be diminished.

ABBREVIATIONS

AHAR	Annual Homeless Assessment Report
BIA	Bureau of Indian Affairs
CDBG	Community Development Block Grant
CHALENG	Community Homelessness Assessment Local Education and Networking Groups
CoC	Continuum of Care
CICH	Collaborative Initiative to Help End Chronic Homelessness
DHS	Department of Homeland Security
Education	Department of Education
ESG	Emergency Shelter Grant
ESEA	Elementary and Secondary Education Act of 1965
HEARTH	Homeless Emergency Assistance and Rapid Transition to Housing Act of 2009

HHS   Department of Health and Human Services
HMIS   Homelessness Management Information System
HUD   Department of Housing and Urban Development
Labor   Department of Labor
NAHASDA Native American Housing Assistance and Self-
             Determination Act
PATH   Projects for Assistance in Transition from Homelessness
PIT   Point-in-Time
RHYMIS   Runaway and Homeless Youth Management Information System
USDA   Department of Agriculture
VA   Department of Veterans Affairs
VASH   VA Supportive Housing

July 20, 2010
Congressional Committees

Homelessness has sometimes been characterized as the "extreme end of poverty."[1] In rural areas of the United States, homelessness has not attracted the same level of attention as in urban areas, although research has shown that the highest poverty rates occur in rural areas as well as center cities. Although some studies have examined the issue of homelessness in rural areas, little comprehensive data exist on the extent of homelessness in these areas or the extent to which various federal programs meet the needs of those experiencing homelessness in rural areas or support providers that serve this population. The Homeless Emergency Assistance and Rapid Transition to Housing (HEARTH) Act of 2009 created the Rural Housing Stability Grant Program.[2] This grant program is seen as to allow rural areas more flexibility to identify and address the needs of persons experiencing homelessness or those in the worst housing situations and reserves Department of Housing and Urban Development (HUD) funding for which rural communities may apply separately.

The HEARTH Act also directed GAO to conduct a broad study of homelessness in rural areas, including tribal lands and colonias.[3] In this report, we provide information about rural homelessness issues, based in significant part on our work in rural areas within six states. Specifically, the report addresses the following questions:

1. What are the characteristics of homelessness in rural areas?
2. What assistance is available to individuals or families experiencing homelessness and what amount of funding have the federal departments and agencies awarded to organizations that assist persons experiencing homelessness in rural areas?
3. What barriers do persons experiencing homelessness and homeless service providers encounter when seeking assistance or funding to provide assistance?

To address these questions, we conducted a review of relevant reports, studies, and our prior research. We also conducted site visits in Arizona, Kentucky, Maine, Minnesota, New Mexico, and Texas. During these visits, we interviewed federal, state, and local housing and homelessness officials and nonprofit homelessness organizations, and toured rural areas in which homelessness was present. We selected the site visit locations based on several factors, including (1) discussions with knowledgeable individuals in the field of homelessness, (2) a review of studies and reports on local and state efforts to serve the homeless in rural areas, (3) the presence of tribal lands and colonias, and (4) geographical diversity. We also reviewed relevant laws, regulations, and program documentation and interviewed officials from various federal agencies as well as national stakeholder organizations. For purposes of this report, we did not limit ourselves to any one federal definition of homelessness and did not specify a specific definition when speaking with researchers, providers, and relevant government officials, but they did clarify on how they defined homelessness in the context of their comments.

We conducted this performance audit from July 2009 to July 2010 in accordance with generally accepted government auditing standards. Those standards require that we plan and perform the audit to obtain sufficient, appropriate evidence to provide a reasonable basis for our findings and conclusions based on our audit objectives. We believe that the evidence obtained provides a reasonable basis for our findings and conclusions based on our audit objectives.

BACKGROUND

Several federal programs—mainstream and targeted—may be available to assist those experiencing homelessness in rural and nonrural areas. Mainstream programs—such as Temporary Assistance for Needy Families, public housing, the Supplemental Nutrition Assistance Program, Medicaid, and the Workforce Investment Act—provide a wide range of assistance, such as cash assistance, housing, food, health care, and job training, for low-income people including those experiencing homelessness. Targeted programs—such as the Emergency Shelter Grant and Runaway and Homeless Youth programs—also provide a range of services but are designed specifically for individuals or families experiencing homelessness.[4]

The McKinney-Vento Homeless Assistance Act (McKinney-Vento) is the principal federal legislation designed to provide funding for shelter and services to persons experiencing homelessness.[5] McKinney-Vento originally consisted of 15 programs providing, among other things, resources for emergency shelter, transitional housing, job training, primary health care, education, and permanent housing. The current act has been amended several times and was most recently reauthorized by the HEARTH Act. For the most part, these amendments have expanded the scope and strengthened the provisions of the original legislation by expanding eligible activities and creating new programs.

This legislation continues to represent the primary source of funding for targeted programs serving persons experiencing homelessness. HUD administers both competitive and formula-based McKinney-Vento programs that fund activities to address homelessness in rural and nonrural areas. HUD's competitively awarded homeless programs comprise the "Continuum of Care" (CoC) system. According to HUD, the program is based on the understanding that homelessness is not caused solely by a lack of shelter, but also involves other physical, social, and economic needs.

Through the CoC system HUD allocates homeless assistance grants to organizations that participate in homeless assistance program planning networks. The planning network or CoC refers to a group of providers and key stakeholders in a geographical area—a city, a county, a metropolitan area, or an entire state—that join to plan for the homeless housing and service system within that geographic area and apply for HUD's competitive homeless program funding.[6] Rural areas typically organize into regional or balance-of-state (areas in the state not already covered by other continuums) CoC systems which may include a mixture of rural and nonrural areas.

Areas in 37 states or territories are organized as balanceof-state CoCs, while other states such as Minnesota and Nebraska have organized into regional CoC systems. Several other federal agencies also have programs targeting homelessness that primarily provide supportive services—including the Departments of Education (Education), Homeland Security (DHS), Labor

(Labor), Justice (DOJ), Health and Human Services (HHS), and Veterans Affairs (VA).[7]

McKinney-Vento also authorized the creation of the US Interagency Council on Homelessness (Interagency Council), which currently includes 19 member agencies.[8] McKinney-Vento mandated that the Interagency Council identify duplication in federal programs and provide assistance to states, local governments, and other public and private nonprofit organizations to enable them to serve those experiencing homelessness more effectively.

The HEARTH Act revises the Interagency Council's mission to coordinate the federal response to homelessness and create a national partnership at every level of government and with the private sector to reduce and end homelessness.[9] HEARTH also mandates that the Interagency Council develop and annually update a national strategic plan to end homelessness.

The Interagency Council's plan, which was released in June 2010, aims to align federal resources effectively and appropriately with four key goals: (1) prevent and end homelessness for families, youth, and children; (2) prevent and end homelessness among veterans; (3) end chronic homelessness; and (4) "set a path" to end all types of homelessness.

As described in our June 2010 report, federal programs define homelessness differently. HUD administers programs under McKinneyVento that specifically target persons experiencing "literal" homelessness (that is, living in shelters or in places not meant for human habitation, but not in precarious housing situations).[10]

According to HUD officials, Congress directs federal agencies as to which definition of homelessness shall be used within each program; furthermore, as HUD's housing resources are not an entitlement, funding must be targeted to those most in need.[11] The statutory definition of homelessness for Education, DOJ, and some HHS targeted programs is broader than that for HUD programs.

For example, under McKinney-Vento, the Education for Homeless Children and Youth program's definition of homelessness includes children and youth who are living in substandard housing, while the Healthcare for the Homeless program's definition includes those who are "doubled up," or living temporarily with another household because they cannot afford housing of their own.[12] Table 1 categorizes definitions of homelessness across federal agencies with targeted homeless assistance programs. In our June 2010 report, we recommended that Education, HHS, and HUD develop a common vocabulary for homelessness and determine if the benefits of collecting data on housing status in targeted and mainstream programs would exceed the costs.

Table 1. Typology of Definitions of "Homelessness" among Federal Agencies with Targeted Homeless Assistance Programs, as of July 2010

Federal agency	Homelessness definition		
	McKinney-Vento individual[a]	McKinney-Vento children and youth[b]	Other [c]
Education		●	
DHS	●		
Labor	●		
DOJ			●
HHS			●
HUD	●		
VA[d]	●		●

[a] Someone who lacked a fixed, regular, and adequate nighttime residence or has a nighttime residence that is a supervised shelter designed to provide temporary accommodations; an institution providing a temporary residence for individuals awaiting institutionalization; or a place not designed for, nor ordinarily used as, a regular sleeping accommodation.

[b] Children and youths who meet the McKinney-Vento individual definition or those who are sharing the housing of other persons due to loss of housing, economic hardship, or similar reasons (doubled up); living in motels, hotels, trailer parks, or camping grounds due to the lack of alternative adequate accommodations; awaiting foster care placement; or living in substandard housing.

[c] Definitions of homelessness other than McKinney-Vento individuals or children and youth definitions. For example, HHS' Runaway and Youth Act's Transitional Living program defines a homeless youth as being generally from the ages of 16 to 22, unable to live in a safe environment with a relative, and lacking any safe alternative living arrangements.

[d] VA definitions depend on the program.

The HEARTH Act broadens the McKinney-Vento definition of "homeless individual," and also defined the terms "homeless," "homeless person," and "homeless individual with a disability."[13]

Federal agencies also do not employ a single definition of "rural" and the definitions generally are not comparable across agencies. In a prior GAO report, we discussed the three most common federal definitions of rural— from the Bureau of the Census, the Department of Agriculture's (USDA)

Economic Research Service, and the Office of Management and Budget—which have differing criteria, such as population threshold or proximity to urban areas.[14] However, even within one measure such as population threshold, different agencies can use different parameters and therefore identify different areas as rural.

The mandate for this report in the HEARTH Act identifies two distinct communities to be included in this review of homelessness in rural areas—tribal lands and colonias. Because the federal government has a unique legal and political relationship with Native American tribes and Alaska Native entities, the administration of housing, homeless assistance, and supportive service programs on tribal lands differs. Federal agencies that have distinct roles and responsiblities to these groups include the Bureau of Indian Affairs (BIA), HUD, and HHS. BIA-administered programs include social services, economic development, housing improvement, and disaster relief. HUD's Office of Native American Programs is responsible for the implementation and administration of programs, such as housing and community development, that are specific to Native Americans and Alaska Natives. The Indian Health Service within HHS is responsible for providing federal health services to Native Americans and Alaska Natives.

Unlike Native Americans and Alaska Natives, the federal government does not have a unique legal and political relationship with colonias. However, the Cranston-Gonzalez Act of 1990 recognized colonias within US borders as distressed communities and designated set-aside funding to advance opportunities for homeownership and economic self-sufficiency in these areas.[15] Individuals and families in colonias may lack safe, sanitary, and sound housing and be without basic services such as potable water, adequate sewage systems, utilities, and paved roads.

Forms of Rural Homelessness Encompass Situations Ranging from the More Visible, Such as Living in Shelters, to the Less Visible, Such as Living in Overcrowded Housing or Outdoors

The characteristics or forms of homelessness in the rural areas we visited ranged from the more visible, such as living in shelters, to the less visible, such as living in overcrowded or substandard housing. The range of living situations of persons experiencing homelessness in rural areas may overlap with the living situations of those experiencing homelessness in nonrural areas. Some persons experiencing homelessness lived in shelters or transitional housing. Shelters, where they existed, provided one of the visible entry points to receiving both housing assistance and supportive services. Some shelters we visited conduct initial assessments of individuals and families experiencing homelessness to determine their needs. The shelters may provide case management or mental health services or provide referrals to services within the area. We also observed various shelter types—some served specific groups, such as domestic violence victims or youth, while others were multipurpose. Some shelters were traditional, small communal shelters; some organizations used scattered site housing as shelters; and some shelters had no fixed location. For example, some service providers issued hotel vouchers, while others had moving shelters in which churches or other organizations would offer space. The shelter would be located in one organization's donated space for a set period of time before moving to another organization. Services available to clients also varied greatly among shelters. Some shelters offered a full range of on-site services such as mental health services, substance abuse treatment, case management, and job training. Other shelters offered limited services or lacked the funding to pay for 24-hour staff. Some areas without shelters relied on volunteers for homeless services because of limited or nonexistent funding.

Other forms of homelessness we observed or heard about in rural areas we visited included persons who owned or rented substandard housing or had established temporary alternative living arrangements such as doubling-up (short stays with persons who offer space). In some rural areas, infrastructure challenges contributed to substandard housing. For example, we observed some houses built in floodplains in colonias we visited in Texas. Additionally, building codes may not exist or may not be enforced in some rural areas. We also observed houses with boarded-up windows, caved-in floors or ceilings, and dangerous alternative heating sources in rural areas in several states. Persons living in similar housing in urban areas may more easily be identified as literally homeless as such structures could be condemned. Some individuals and families in rural areas lived in overcrowded homes, sometimes with multiple generations living together. In some places we visited, we heard that doubling-up or multigenerational living was a cultural norm or an accepted practice because people "take care of their own." Some people had very few options. For example, on tribal lands many families have lived for long periods in overcrowded housing because waiting lists for housing are extremely long and private financing is rare due to legal issues with land ownership. Tribal officials from the Pueblo of Acoma reservation recently conducted a housing inventory and found approximately 155 overcrowded units on the reservation out of approximately 700 occupied units.[16] Providers told us that severely overcrowded situations often were associated with domestic violence and child abuse. Providers said youth experiencing homelessness often "couch surfed," trading goods or services such as drugs, sex, money, or child care for a temporary stay in someone's home. Not all federal programs include such living conditions in their definitions of homelessness, and persons living in these situations may not be eligible for some federal assistance.

Finally, some individuals and families experiencing homelessness in the rural areas we visited were sleeping in areas not meant for human habitation, including outdoor locations, vehicles, and abandoned buildings. For example:

- On tribal lands in Arizona, we heard of persons living in dry river beds or in outbuildings such as barns or backyard sheds.
- In Maine, we were informed of year-round encampments in the woods. In one case, the local fire department inspected and sanctioned a large fire pit for an encampment with the intent of minimizing the number of smaller pits.
- In Minnesota, we observed abandoned buses and ice houses that were used by persons without regular shelter and heard from a previously homeless woman about how she built a structure using a pallet, a large cardboard box, and a tarp to keep out the rain. She told us that she placed the structure in an old mining pit to avoid detection.

These individuals meet both the existing McKinney-Vento and HEARTH Act definitions of homeless and could be eligible for federal assistance. However with a limited number of shelters or other outreach, they may not be accessing services. Providers and persons experiencing homelessness emphasized that some persons experiencing homelessness wanted to remain hidden as they often were sought by abusive partners, parents, creditors, or the police. In the case of some families, parents were afraid that their children would be taken from them by social services.

Challenges in Collecting Comprehensive Data Make Understanding the Extent of Homelessness in Rural and Nonrural Areas Difficult

Due to limited comprehensive data and challenges in combining data from different federal sources, understanding the extent of homelessness in rural and nonrural areas is difficult. Several agencies are required to collect data on segments of the homeless population, but as described in our June 2010 report, these data have shortcomings and do not fully describe the incidence and prevalence of homelessness in rural or nonrural areas.[17] HUD developed two sources of data—the Homelessness Management Information System (HMIS) and the biennial Point-in-Time (PIT) count—for understanding the extent of homelessness. These data are reported to Congress annually for the Annual Homeless Assessment Report (AHAR) on the extent and nature of homelessness in the United States. Under the direction of Congress, HUD created a set of technical data collection standards for local HMIS, instructed programs receiving HUD McKinney-Vento funding to report to those local systems, and encouraged all programs for homeless people, regardless of their funding source, to report data to HMIS.[18] HMIS records and stores client-level information on the characteristics (on an ongoing basis throughout the year) and service needs of homeless persons and the data are used to produce counts of the sheltered homeless population over a full year. In addition to HMIS, the PIT counts of both sheltered and unsheltered homeless populations are based on the number of persons experiencing homelessness on a single night during the last week in January (every other year), and the data are included as part of the CoC applications, which are submitted to HUD annually.[19] CoCs conduct a PIT count every other year with 452 CoCs completing a count in 2009. PIT counts include the "street counts" that estimate the number of unsheltered homeless people in each community, as well as estimates of sheltered homeless people based on a census of shelter and transitional housing occupants on a particular night.

Although other programs are encouraged to report data to HMIS, agencies such as HHS, Education, and VA have their own systems for collecting data. For example, HHS's Runaway and Homeless Youth Management Information System (RHYMIS) collects demographic and service data on runaway and homeless youth being served by HHS's Family and Youth Services Bureau's programs. To demonstrate compliance with the Elementary and Secondary Education Act of 1965 (ESEA), as amended, Education collects data on homeless children and youth served by ESEA programs and the Education of Homeless Children and Youth program through the Consolidated State Performance Report. The McKinney-Vento Act requires local school districts to have Homelessness Liaisons, provide appropriate services and support, and collect and report data to Education annually. Additionally, through VA's Northeast Program Evaluation Center, VA collects data on each individual veteran that enters one of VA's specialized homeless veterans programs. And, through the Community Homelessness Assessment Local Education and Networking Groups (CHALENG) process, VA collects population-based data by conducting local community group surveys with VA staff and community participants. CHALENG data is nationally compiled in an annual report to provide prevalence estimates of veteran homelessness and to assess the needs of the population as well as gaps in local services. Lastly, the Census Bureau's decennial population and housing census collects data on places in which the homeless population receive services as well as targeted nonshelter outdoor locations. While the Census makes an effort to count all residents, including those experiencing homelessness, the 2010 Census does not plan to report a separate count of the population experiencing homelessness or a count of the population who use homelessness services, and the Census Bureau advises against using its data on homelessness from the 2000 Census.

Because of different statutory requirements for each federal agency— including data collection requirements and differences in definitions— these data do not reflect the full extent of homelessness in rural or nonrural areas. Each agency focuses on the segments of the homeless population that the agency serves, resulting in incompatible data for comparison and analysis. For example, HHS's Runaway and Homeless Youth Program, for which data is collected in RHYMIS, focuses on the runaway and homeless youth being served by the Basic Center Program, the Transitional Living Program for Older Homeless Youth, and contacts made by the Street Outreach Program grantees. HHS provides homeless assistance to adult individuals and families through programs such as Health Care for the Homeless, Projects for Assistance in Transition from Homelessness (PATH), Grants for the Benefits of Homeless Individuals, and Service in Supportive Housing. All of these programs collect data on their relevant populations based on statutory requirements.[20] VA collects data on homeless veterans as part of its annual CHALENG survey, in accordance with different statutory requirements.[21] However, in December 2009, HHS established an agreement with HUD for PATH providers to move towards reporting under the HMIS. Also, according to HUD officials, there has been an initial evaluation of aligning some of VA's homelessness data with HUD's homelessness data.

The varying definitions of "homelessness" and "rural"—as well as the extent to which "rural" is reported—also limit the ability to understand the incidence and prevalence of homelessness in rural areas. For example, according to officials, doubled-up persons are included in some VA and HHS program definitions but excluded from HUD's definition. Thus, data on homelessness are captured differently across federal agencies. Similarly, although our work did not focus on potential reasons for the different definitions, these differences across federal programs make comparing the extent of homelessness in rural and nonrural areas difficult. For instance, HUD's AHAR formally classifies locations into two groups— principal cities and suburban or rural areas. Specifically, HUD estimates that about 1.56 million people were homeless in emergency shelters or transitional housing at some point during fiscal year 2009. More than two-thirds (or about 1.1 million) of them were located in principal cities, while one-third (or about 0.5 million) were in suburban or rural jurisdictions. HHS's RHYMIS and VA's CHALENG do not break out the counts of homelessness between rural and nonrural areas.

HUD's PIT count is the only data collection effort designed to obtain a national count of those experiencing homelessness, and while a more in-depth discussion of the difficulties associated with collecting the data can be found in our June 2010 report, there are some additional challenges particular to rural areas.

- Persons experiencing homelessness are inherently difficult to count. They are mobile, can seek shelter in secluded areas, and may not wish to attract the notice of local government officials. Moreover, rural areas are often large and have widely dispersed populations and difficult-to-reach locations, exacerbating the difficulties of finding and counting persons experiencing homelessness, including those who do not necessarily want to be found.

- Count methodologies vary by CoCs and might not be well implemented. Service providers who conduct the PIT counts are meeting their mandated requirements under McKinney-Vento. However, with no funding to pay for the count, service providers often rely on volunteers to meet an unfunded mandate. Particularly in areas of the United States where average temperatures are below freezing in January, finding unsheltered persons and recruiting volunteers to count them becomes difficult. Although HUD officials told us that the benefit of a January count relates to the increased demand for shelters at the coldest time of year, homeless shelters and services are limited in rural areas, and in some counties, nonexistent. In a few of the states we visited, commitments from state and local officials and advocates have enhanced the process, resulting in an ability to recruit volunteers and local organizations who have built a trusting relationship with homeless populations.

According to officials and service providers in the states we visited, HUD's PIT count likely has undercounted the rural homeless population, but to what extent is unknown. While HUD officials acknowledge the shortcomings of their counts, they believe significant progress has been made in recent years in collecting homelessness data, particularly their estimate annually since 2005 of the extent of homelessness and their efforts to ensure data quality through providing technical assistance.[22]

Another factor associated with the completeness of federal agency data is the lack of migration data. According to federal agency officials and service providers, very little is known about the migration between rural and nonrural areas of those experiencing homelessness because there is no requirement or formal system for tracking migration patterns. Although no federal programs formally track or are required to track migration information, some local service providers maintain that information for their own purposes. For example, the Kentucky Housing Corporation, beginning in 2009, included questionnaires to track migration within and across states. Those experiencing homelessness may migrate to and from nonrural areas for many reasons. For example, service providers told us that persons experiencing homelessness in rural areas have migrated to nonrural areas following a job loss, to reconnect with families, and to obtain supportive services. Conversely, people have migrated from nonrural areas to rural areas to connect with families and, in the case of tribal lands, to receive services. Furthermore, because persons experiencing homelessness are more mobile, and formal migration data do not exist, the potential exists for duplicated counts—complicating any comparison of the extent of homelessness between rural and nonrural areas.

Several Federal Agencies Fund Programs through State Intermediaries or Local Homeless Providers That Assist Persons Experiencing Homelessness in Rural Areas

Several federal agencies fund programs, through state intermediaries or local homeless providers, which are targeted to the homelessness population or which assist low income persons and families including those experiencing homelessness. Some federal programs specifically target homelessness, while others assist low income persons and families, including those experiencing homelessness, or include assistance for persons experiencing homelessness among eligible uses. In total, these programs fund permanent and short term housing and a variety of supportive services such as mental health services, substance abuse treatment, case management, and job training.

Federal programs		Category of services				
		Housing		Supportive services		
		Permanent[a]	Short term[b]	Food	Health[c]	Other[d]
HUD	Single Room Occupancy	●				
	Shelter Plus Care[e]	●				
	Supportive Housing Program	●	●	●	●	●
	HUD-VA Supportive Housing[f]	●			●	
	Emergency Shelter Grant		●	●	●	●
	Native American Housing Assistance and Self Determination Act	●				
	Self-help Homeownership Opportunity Program	●				
	HOME Investment Partnerships	●	●			
	Community Development Block Grant	●	●			
	Housing Choice Voucher (Section 8)	●				
	Public Housing	●				
HHS	Runaway and Homeless Youth		●	●	●	●
	Projects for Assistance in Transition from Homelessness		●		●	●
	Health Care for the Homeless				●	
	Federal Surplus Real Property[g]	●	●			
	Grants for the Benefits of Homeless Individuals				●	●
	Services in Supportive Housing				●	●
	Medicaid				●	
	Temporary Assistance for Needy Families					●
	Headstart				●	●
VA	Grant & Per Diem		●	●	●	●
	Health Care for Homeless Veterans				●	
	Domiciliary Care for Homeless Veterans				●	
	HUD-VA Supportive Housing[h]	●			●	
	Medical Centers				●	●
	Disability Compensation					●
Labor	Homeless Veterans Reintegration Program					●
	Workforce Investment Act					●
Education	Education for Homeless Children and Youth				●	●
DOJ	Transitional Housing Assistance for Child Victims of Domestic Violence, Stalking, or Sexual Assault		●			
DHS	Emergency Food and Shelter		●	●		
BIA	Human services programs such as Welfare Assistance, Housing Improvement and others	●				●
USDA	Housing programs such as Single-Family Housing and Multi-family housing	●				
	Community Facilities Loan		●			
	Food programs such as Supplemental Nutrition Assistance Program; Special Supplemental Nutrition Program for Women, Infants, and Children; school meals; Commodity Supplemental Food Program; and others			●		
IRS	Low Income Housing Tax Credit	●				
SSA	SSI, SSI-Disability					●

☐ Mainstream or nontargeted programs
▨ Programs targeted at homelessness

Source: GAO.

[a] Permanent refers to permanent supportive or affordable housing.

[b] Short term refers to emergency or short-term shelters. Examples include homeless shelters, domestic violence shelters, transitional housing, and hotel vouchers.

[c] Examples include mental health services, physical health services, substance abuse treatment, residential treatment, and case management.

[d] Examples include general or cash assistance, job training, employment assistance, education, child care and development, and transportation assistance.

[e] Although the Shelter Plus Care program does not pay for supportive services, recipients must match each dollar of funding for housing with a dollar of funding for supportive services.

[f] HUD-VA Supportive Housing is a joint program in which HUD funds the housing and VA funds the supportive services.

[g] The Federal Surplus Real Property program, established by title V of McKinney-Vento, provides surplus land or buildings in support of persons experiencing homelessness. These properties can be used for housing and a wide range of supportive services but the program provides no monetary support for any activity. See 42 USC. § 11411.

Figure 1. Federal Programs That May Benefit Persons Experiencing Homelessness in Rural Areas.

Targeted homeless funding is often further targeted to segments of the population such as youth or veterans. See figure 1 for examples of targeted and mainstream or nontargeted programs that may benefit persons experiencing homelessness and the types of assistance available under each program.

HUD funds programs targeted to the homeless populations through state or local entities for the Emergency Shelter Grant (ESG) program and to providers who participate in CoCs. The ESG program is dispersed by formula, while three grant programs—the Single Room Occupancy, Shelter Plus Care, and Supportive Housing programs—are awarded competitively through the CoC process.[23] HUD receives a single appropriation for its targeted programs and administratively determines the amount of funding for the ESG program.[24] ESG funding is awarded based on the Community Development Block Grant (CDBG) formula, which designates that 70 percent of funding is awarded directly to entitlement cities and counties and 30 percent is awarded to state entities that determine the dispersion of funding for the more rural parts of the state.[25] Organizations located in areas or municipalities not receiving direct ESG allocations compete for funding through the state entity. For example in 2009 in Maine, only Portland received its own allocation of about $94,000, while organizations from all other areas or municipalities within the state competed for about $770,000.

HUD's three competitive homeless assistance grants are awarded through the CoC process using a scoring system where HUD scores the planning document submitted by the CoCs as part of the application.[26] Programs that have previously received funding, referred to as renewals, receive a higher funding priority and are funded before new programs are considered for funding. In 2008, 86 percent of the competitive homeless assistance grants were renewals. Although CoC funding is awarded competitively, HUD determines a need factor called the pro rata need (also based on the CDBG formula) for each CoC. According to a HUD official, in calculating the preliminary pro rata need, HUD allocates 75 percent of funding to entitlement cities and counties that qualify for direct ESG allocations and 25 percent of funding to all other areas.[27] All CoCs have an identified need factor, but CoCs may not have funded programs as new funding is awarded in order of CoC score, which is based on multiple factors.

HHS and other federal agencies—including Education, Labor, VA, DHS, and DOJ—largely operate their targeted programs through state entities or by directly funding community-based public or nonprofit entities. HHS provides funding for a number of programs, including Runaway and Homeless Youth, Health Care for the Homeless, and PATH. Funding for Health Care for the

Homeless is distributed competitively, while PATH funding is distributed to states, Washington, D.C. and US territories that distribute the funding. The PATH formula, which has remained unchanged since 1990, primarily considers the urban population of the state or territory and designates a minimum of $300,000 for states and $50,000 for territories. In 2009, 18 states and the District of Columbia received the state minimum. DHS, through the Federal Emergency Management Agency, funds the Emergency Food and Shelter Program, which distributes funding to local entities through the United Way of America or similarly functioning organizations. Funding is formula-based and considers poverty rate and unemployment. Some providers in very small communities told us that they receive federal funding only through the Emergency Food and Shelter Program.

Mainstream federal programs may assist persons experiencing homelessness but the level of assistance directed towards homelessness is generally unknown as some programs are not required to track if participants have been or are experiencing homelessness. Mainstream programs provide assistance to individuals and families and include HHS' Temporary Assistance for Needy Families; USDA's food programs such as the Supplemental Nutrition Assistance Program and the Special Supplemental Nutrition Program for Women, Infants, and Children; HUD's housing programs such as public housing and the Housing Choice Voucher program; the Social Security Administration's Supplemental Security Income and disability insurance programs; and VA's disability compensation program.

Funding in other federal programs also may be used for homeless assistance based on the decisions of state, local, or tribal governments. Homeless programs are one of many eligible uses for funding in programs such as HUD's CDBG program and USDA's Community Facilities Loan program. CDBG is formula-based with state entities receiving and dispersing the portion of funding intended for rural areas, while the Community Facilities Loan program is awarded competitively through USDA's state offices. Some programs direct funding to areas that are in particular need of housing infrastructure. For example, the Cranston-Gonzalez Act requires states that share a border with Mexico to set aside CDBG funds for the colonias. This funding may be used to expand water and sewer services and to provide housing assistance.[28] USDA's agency for rural development also funds programs to improve infrastructure in the colonias.

Tribes receive funding for housing, health care, and other services through HUD's Native American Housing Assistance and Self-Determination Act (NAHASDA) programs and a variety of programs offered through HHS and

BIA. These programs, although not specifically targeted at homelessness, may assist persons experiencing homelessness. They are available to recognized tribes only and funding generally is formulaic, based on tribal enrollment. Generally, NAHASDA money is distributed to tribal-designated housing entities that use money to build or refurbish housing. BIA programs are funded as contracts awarded to designated tribal entities to provide a range of services. In both cases, tribal governments determine priorities, usage, and eligibility. Housing funds are distributed to regional BIA offices through a formula process and individuals receive assistance based on priority until funds are exhausted.

Limited Data Are Available on the Amount of Targeted and Nontargeted Assistance to Rural Versus Nonrural Areas

The amount of federal funding for targeted homeless assistance programs in rural areas is uncertain. According to the Congressional Research Service, in fiscal year 2009 federal agencies spent more than $2.85 billion on programs targeted to address the needs of individuals and families experiencing homelessness.[29]

HUD's targeted homeless programs represent the largest funding source for federal targeted homeless assistance, which for fiscal year 2009 totaled more than $1.7 billion or more than 62 percent of total targeted funding. Figure 2 shows the targeted funding by federal agency. We were unable to determine the total portion of this funding that went to rural areas.

Determining what funding went to rural areas is difficult because some federal agencies use self-reported data that may not be accurate, do not distinguish between rural and nonrural areas, or do not track whether funding went to such areas. As discussed earlier in this report, federal agencies use multiple definitions of rural, complicating any determination of what types of areas received funding.

For instance, HUD's CoC programs maintain data on the amount of assistance for rural areas; however, grant applicants could designate (self-identify)—based on a HUD provided definition of rural area—whether they were in rural areas or not. Table 2 shows the funding based on this designation for fiscal years 2006- 2008. In fiscal year 2008, according to the HUD data, 9.3 percent of CoC funding went to rural areas, which represented about 15 percent of total projects.

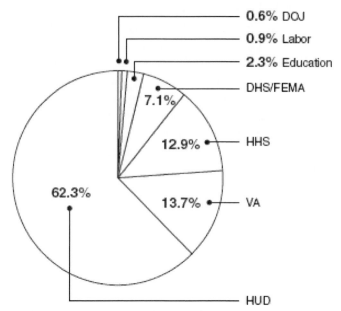

Source: GAO analysis of Congressional Research Service data
Note: Data do not include assistance from mainstream programs which may also
    provide support to persons experiencing homelessness.

Figure 2. Percent of Total Federal Funding Targeting Homelessness by Agency for
Fiscal Year 2009.

**Table 2. Rural Funding within HUD's CoC Programs, Based on Grant
Applicant Reporting as Rural or Not**

Fiscal year	Total funding awarded in billions	Funding awarded to rural projects in millions (percentage of total)	Total projects funded	Rural projects funded(percentage of total)
2008	$1.40	$129.9	6336	960
		(9.3%)		(15.2%)
2007	1.33	99.82	5911	718
		(7.5)		(12.2)
2006	1.21	69.82	5288	538
		(5.8)		(10.2)

Source: GAO analysis of HUD data.

Similarly, VA can determine spending levels in rural areas for its grant and per diem program using self-reported data. Table 3 shows funding and the number of beds based on this designation for fiscal years 2007-2009. In fiscal year 2009, according to VA data, 13.5 percent of capital grant awards under the Grant and Per Diem program funding went to rural areas, which represented 8.5 percent of the funded beds. HUD's ESG program targets 30 percent of its funding toward nonentitlement cities or counties, which represent more rural areas. However, according to HUD, ESG provides discretion to the state entity to decide how to allocate ESG funds. A state may limit funds to nonentitlement areas and metropolitan cities and urban counties that did not receive individual allocations, or may choose to fund entitlement cities and counties that received direct allocations from HUD.

Table 3. Urban and Rural Fiscal Year Funding for VA's Capital Grant Awards for the Grant and Per Diem Program Based on Grant Applicant Reporting as Rural or Not

		2009	2008	2007	Total
Funding in millions	Urban	$11.67	$29.14	$11.3	*$52.11*
(percentage of total)		(68.9%)	(82.1%)	(77.1%)	
	Rural	2.28	4.1	3.35	*9.73*
		(13.5)	(11.6)	(22.9)	
	Unidentified	3	2.24	0	*5.24*
		(17.7)	(6.3)	(0)	
	Total	*$16.95*	*$35.48*	*$14.65*	*$67.08*
Beds	Urban	827	1337	691	*2855*
(percentage of total)		(71.8)	(88.2)	(80.1)	
	Rural	98	127	172	*397*
		(8.5)	(8.4)	(19.9)	
	Unidentified	227	52	0	*279*
		(19.7)	(3.4)	(0)	
	Total	*1152*	*1516*	*863*	*3531*

Source: VA.
Note: Percentages may not add to 100 percent due to rounding.

Other agencies also maintain limited information on the amount of targeted homeless funding that is allocated to rural or nonrural areas. Depending on the program, HHS and Education do not track whether funding is for providers or projects in rural or nonrural areas. Labor has two size categories within its targeted Homeless Veterans' Reintegration program, one for urban areas and one for nonurban areas, with different dollar amounts available. However, Labor officials said their definition of nonurban was an area with less than 569,463 persons, which is at least 10 times the population limit specified in other agencies' definitions of rural.[30]

Similarly, funding information on the mainstream and other nontargeted programs that can provide support to individuals or families experiencing homelessness is limited. Individuals and families who meet the qualifications for services under mainstream programs are eligible regardless of whether they live in rural, tribal, or nonrural areas. Some mainstream programs, such as Temporary Assistance for Needy Families, that may offer assistance to individuals or families experiencing homelessness are not required to track housing status, which prevents a determination of how much funding went to persons in rural and nonrural areas. For other nontargeted programs, funding for homelessness is often difficult to disaggregate from other spending. For example, HUD's CDBG funds have many eligible uses as well as usage clauses that required a certain percentage of funding to be used for projects that benefit low-income persons. The building of shelters and transitional housing are among several eligible uses that would assist persons experiencing homelessness; however, the total amount of assistance to specific types of projects is unknown. A certain percentage of CDBG funds for states bordering Mexico are targeted to the colonias, but the amount of funding that specifically addresses homelessness is unknown. For NAHASDA and other programs that fund assistance to tribal entities, individual tribal governments determine usage and disaggregating funds used for persons experiencing homelessness would need to be done at the tribal level. However, USDA, which has nonfood programs that primarily serve rural areas, was able to disaggregate funding within its Community Facilities Loan Program. Eligible uses under this program include homeless and domestic violence shelters, community centers, and fire stations. For fiscal years 2004-2009, the program financed a total of 7 homeless shelters and 76 domestic violence shelters for a total of about $29.7 million of the program's $4.5 billion total for those years.

We were unable to determine whether the distribution of federal funding for supporting persons experiencing homelessness was proportional to need in rural and nonrural areas. Such a determination would require complete data on the total number of persons experiencing homelessness in both rural and nonrural areas, as well as reliable information on the funding available in both rural and nonrural areas. We found that the counts of homelessness are not complete for this purpose, and as stated above, funding levels are nondeterminable for a variety of reasons.

Barriers to the Rural Homeless Population Seeking Assistance Include Limited Availability of Services, Lack of Transportation, and Lack of Affordable Housing

According to state and local officials, as well as individuals experiencing homelessness we interviewed in the states we visited, limited availability of services, lack of transportation, and lack of affordable housing have been some common barriers that the rural homeless population encounters when seeking assistance. Factors such as geography, population density, and socio-economic conditions also can make access to services challenging in rural areas— particularly when considered in combination with the barriers cited above.

Providers we spoke to in the states we visited said homeless shelters and transitional housing in rural areas are scarce and serve a wide geographical area, and in some instances, counties do not have shelters. A shelter we visited in Maine with 63 beds is the only multi-purpose shelter that serves the entire homeless population in a county of nearly 1,000 square miles. In addition, 4 of the 16 counties in Maine are without emergency shelters, with 1 of those 4 counties using hotels as an alternative in the winter. Some shelters may dedicate services to a specific subpopulation such as youth, domestic violence, and substance abuse clients, which could narrow the availability of assistance for some individuals or populations. Many of the providers with whom we spoke have had to turn away individuals and families because their shelters were full and backlogged. According to officials in Maine, between June and August 2009, shelters across the state turned away 500 families, including a total of 200 children. Because shelters are one of the visible points of entry to a network of services such as health care, alcohol and drug treatment, job training, and case managers, those experiencing homelessness in rural areas who are without shelters may be more likely to be disconnected from caseworkers who can provide referrals to these supportive services. However, community action agencies, faith-based organizations, and other nongovernmental entities may offer assistance to networks of services. Similarly, supportive services, such as medical and dental, mental health, food, and job training, are also limited in rural areas. For example, one service provider in rural Kentucky stated that the closest mental health center was 50 minutes away, while another service provider in rural Maine told us that the closest psychiatrist was about an hour and a half away. Also in Maine, rural service providers told us that there is no funding to support job training. Furthermore, officials said that domestic violence is associated with homelessness in rural communities and tribal areas, and those individuals have limited resources or services.

According to those we interviewed, the lack of transportation in rural areas has hindered the homeless population in accessing services. Rural areas can be isolating due to the combination of expansive land size and sparse population. Persons experiencing homelessness might be geographically cut-off from the limited homeless service providers available in their area, and would need to travel long distances to receive needed services. Many of the state and local officials, service providers, and individuals experiencing homelessness interviewed told us that public transportation either was nonexistent or limited (i.e., infrequent service and limited coverage areas). If homeless individuals missed their appointments, they have to reschedule for another appointment at a later time thereby delaying services, or their services could be denied according to one service provider in Minnesota. Individuals experiencing homelessness in some of the areas we visited with no public transportation reported that they utilized dial-a-ride services provided by community action agencies or relied on friends or caseworkers. The cost of public transportation can also be an issue for those with very little income, although some local service providers with whom we spoke were able to give bus passes to their clients. Alternatively, some local nonprofits provided automobiles or buses to connect individuals and families to services, but coverage areas also were limited.

According to many of the people we interviewed, persons experiencing homelessness and seeking assistance also may encounter the barrier of limited safe and affordable housing in rural areas. Providers in certain areas of the states we visited raised concerns about the shortage of affordable housing and, in some cases, quality of housing available in the areas, noting that they were aware of some properties that lacked complete plumbing or heat.[31] In some of the rural areas we visited, deteriorating housing conditions for private market units may be more severe due to the absence of building code enforcement. According to a service provider in eastern Kentucky, many homes in the areas are heated with wood or coal (a potential fire hazard), and others lacked complete plumbing. Moreover, because market rents in eastern Kentucky have been so low compared to nonrural areas due to high poverty rates, programs, such as the Low- Income Housing Tax Credits (LIHTC) are examples of financial incentives to attract investors who have shied away from supporting low-income housing development in the area.[32] Furthermore, according to providers we spoke with in Kentucky and Texas, topographic conditions, such as limited flat land in eastern Kentucky and flood plains in the colonias in Webb and Hidalgo counties in Texas, have discouraged investors and developers from investing in these rural areas. According to a service provider in Arizona, development on tribal lands is restricted by legal issues relating to sovereign land, which reduces banks' willingness to finance projects. Resistance in local communities also has presented obstacles to building new housing as described by those we interviewed.

For example, Minnesota state officials noted that some local communities have resisted the building of shelters and other housing for the homeless or low-income populations because they believe that undesirable persons will move to their communities. For similar reasons, a local government in Texas has not sought funds from state or other sources to fund homeless programs, according to a local shelter provider. Compounding the issue of lack of affordable housing, service providers in some of the states we visited have experienced long waiting lists (about 2 years) for the Housing Choice Voucher Program (tenant-based Section 8).[33] For example, service providers in Maine told us that they have not been able to obtain tenant-based Section 8 vouchers since December 2008.

Based on those with whom we spoke and relevant research, individual barriers such as mental health issues, felony records, and no proof of identification have hindered those seeking assistance. According to the 1996 National Survey of Homeless Assistance Providers and Clients, two-thirds of the rural homeless population report having a mental health or substance abuse problem and may require specialized services such as psychiatric referral and treatment.[34] Several individuals with whom we spoke in a shelter indicated that they felt more mentally and emotionally stable after being put on medication received under public health care coverage through the help of shelter staff.

Also, program eligibility and rules may exclude some felons from federal housing assistance, including tenant-based and project-based Section 8 programs. Without federal housing assistance, these individuals could remain homeless because the ability to find a job that would pay for market rent could also be affected by their criminal records.[35] Another individual barrier is the lack of documentation to prove identity. Without birth certificates, driver's licenses, and Social Security cards which, according to some providers with whom we spoke, some persons experiencing homelessness lack, individuals and families might not be able to apply for and obtain services.

Table 4. Possible Needs of the Homeless Population and Potential Corresponding Barriers in Rural Areas

Possible needs	Structural barriers	Applicant-related barriers
Physical housing		
Temporary housing	• No shelters or shelters are full. • Shortage of transitional housing. • Communities' resistance to homeless programs.	• Felons generally do not qualify for federal housing assistance.
Permanent Housing	• Shortage of permanent and permanent supportive housing. • Limited number of tenant-based Section 8 vouchers. • Substandard housing ineligible for tenant-based Section 8 vouchers. • Limited investors for affordable housing development.	• Limited income to pay the difference between actual rent and amount subsidized by tenant-based Section 8 vouchers.
Adequate income to afford housing		
	• Economic environment has resulted in job losses or lower wages. • Lack of public transportation to get to a job.	• Criminal record may discourage employers from hiring people. • Lack of personal identification. • Lack of contact information. • Low educational attainment rate. • Mental health or substance abuse issues not beingtreated.

Possible needs	Structural barriers	Applicant-related barriers
Physical housing		
		• Lack of child care options.
Services		
	• Limited health care providers, including dental and vision care. • Limited mental health providers. • Limited or no substance abuse services. • Limited access to providers. • Limited case managers. • Lack of transportation to get to services.	• May not qualify for services due to program definitions. • Lack of personal identification. • Lack of contact information. • May not seek services due to pride or privacy. • Lack ability to successfully apply for services. • Lack knowledge of available assistance.

Source: GAO.

Table 4 illustrates some examples of barriers for persons experiencing homelessness, as discussed above and further identified in our interviews with local service providers and homeless individuals in the states we visited.

Barriers to the Rural Homeless Service Providers Include Administrative Burden, Lack of Affordable Housing, and Challenges Related to Geography and Population Density

According to state and local officials and local service providers in the states we visited, administrative burden, lack of affordable housing, and challenges related to geography and population density were barriers for rural homeless service providers. Some of the local service providers with whom we spoke indicated that they operated with limited staff and, due to capacity issues, assumed a wide variety of responsibilities from providing direct service to clients to applying for federal and other grants. In particular, service providers in rural areas with whom we spoke have responded to limited resources by applying to, and assembling multiple funding sources from both state and federal programs. As a result, the time consumed in grant writing and meeting the various compliance and review requirements set by statute represented an administrative and workload burden, according to service providers and state officials with whom we spoke. For example, providers in Maine expressed frustration with the duplicative review for the Supportive Housing Grant Program and tenant-based Section 8 Program, both of which HUD administers but under separate authorities. According to some service providers with whom we spoke, many grant applications also require data to demonstrate resource needs. Especially in rural areas with no shelters or visible points of entry for services, counts of the homeless are not documented, and without data it is hard to prove that the services are needed. Because of the administrative burden and challenges in meeting application requirements, some providers with whom we spoke were discouraged from applying for funds from certain programs. A coalition we spoke to in Maine said that many of its members were discouraged by the requirements of programs that received stimulus funds and therefore considered not applying for them. Also, as described in our June 2010 report, issues related to multiple federal definitions of homelessness have posed challenges for service providers.[36] Moreover, according to Minnesota state officials and service providers we spoke with, Minnesota's definition of homelessness is different from some federal programs, creating another level of complexity in understanding the definition and determining client eligibility. According to state officials, Minnesota's definition of homelessness includes those who, as long as the person or family's situation is not stable are doubling up and "couch surfing" for at least a year or four separate occasions over a 3 year period. While this is consistent with a broader definition of homelessness used by Education under the McKinney-Vento Act, it has not been consistent with HUD's definition of chronic homelessness.

State and local officials and rural service providers cited a lack of affordable housing as another challenge for service providers when addressing homelessness in rural areas. Specifically, some of the local service providers with whom we spoke have been unable to move people from emergency shelters, homeless shelters, or transitional housing programs to permanent housing due to shortages of tenant-based Section 8 vouchers and a shortage of affordable housing. According to service providers in multiple locations, due to the shortage in tenant-based Section 8 vouchers, the shelters they work with are full and stays at shelters have lengthened. Without financial assistance, those experiencing homelessness may find it challenging to move out of short-term housing. Furthermore, to the extent that tenant-based Section 8 vouchers have been available, some providers told us in their communities that the current housing stock has been deteriorating and limited new housing units have been built, so there is nowhere for that voucher to be used. According to HUD, between 1995 and 2007, LIHTC—the principal federal subsidy mechanism for supporting the production of new and rehabilitated rental housing for low-income households—were used predominately for new construction. With that said, the number of new construction units has declined since 2005.[37] Moreover, according to HUD regional office officials, the lack of affordable housing also is attributable to the significant reduction in size of the housing projects being built. As a result, some providers told us long waiting lists for tenant-based Section 8 vouchers exist. According to a rural service provider in Kentucky, the tenant-based Section 8 voucher waiting list had 3,000 names on it.

The persons with whom we spoke also consistently said the size of service areas and low population densities in rural areas presented obstacles to service provision. The combination of expansive service areas and sparse populations require many service providers to drive long distances to serve their clients. For example, several rural service providers, particularly case workers, described their vehicles as their offices because of the amount of time they spent traveling between meetings with other service providers and serving clients. Furthermore, according to HUD, because funding is limited, many rural service providers cannot afford large staffs and often wear many hats. In an urban area, separate staff or separate agencies might be responsible for assessing different needs such as housing, nutrition, education, job-search, mental and physical health, and substance abuse needs. However, in a rural area, one individual may be the client's primary point of contact and may have to consider the whole range of issues. Furthermore, some rural areas do not have broadband services and some providers we spoke with said that they are excluded from some of the communications and resources available over the Internet. For instance, HUD regional office officials acknowledged that some rural service providers have been unable to connect to some of their technical assistance workshops and learn about application preparation, project administration, and management.

Local officials and service providers have cited other barriers such as variability of local commitments and diminishing purchasing power. In some of the states we visited, some service providers mentioned variability in local and state commitment, which can influence the homeless assistance programs. For example, 10 years ago Minnesota invested in an intensive case management pilot program which provides housing and supportive services to assist people with long histories of homelessness. Because of the success of the pilot, the Minnesota legislature has continued to appropriate funding to finance supportive housing for five long-term homeless projects in areas that include approximately 80 percent of Minnesota's population, according to a service provider in Minnesota. In contrast, other communities have been resistant to supporting homeless programs, such as one community organization in Texas described that their local government resisted acquiring additional funds in fear of attracting more homeless individuals and families to the community. Diminishing purchasing power also affects the ability of local service providers to address needs in their communities. According to CoC participants, Maine receives PATH funds, but the amount has remained steady at $300,000 per year for the last 17 years. According to officials, the buying power of the program has diminished to $158,000 (in real dollars) today compared to 17 years ago. Similarly, the per diem rate, funded through HUD's ESG program, has diminished from $12.41 in 2008 to $11.21 in 2009, nearly a 10 percent decrease, although service providers in Maine have increased services such as adding more beds in the shelter.[38]

Limited Effective Collaboration among Federal Homelessness Programs Has Hindered Opportunities to Integrate Services

While a few examples of federal collaboration regarding homelessness have demonstrated aspects of effective collaboration, effective collaboration has been limited between HUD and HHS, two of the key federal agencies funding housing and supportive services that include programs for more than one subpopulation. In an October 2005 report, we identified key collaborative practices among federal agencies that include agreeing on roles and responsibilities, defining and articulating a common outcome, establishing mutually reinforcing or joint strategies, and identifying and addressing needs by leveraging resources.[39] Collaboration to link supportive services and housing is particularly significant for rural areas because of the complex system of barriers in rural areas, such as limited bed capacity in shelters, distance to services, and lack of transportation. Such linkage can enhance strategies to address challenges that limited resources and the other barriers pose. One study regarding the linking of affordable housing with supportive services— supportive housing—indicated that over the long term, it could save public resources by reducing the cycle of homelessness through improved housing stability and behavioral health outcomes.[40] Moreover, some studies indicated that offering housing with supportive services resulted in fewer hospital days and emergency room visits, which are publicly provided.[41]

Two completed demonstration projects—Collaborative Initiative to Help End Chronic Homelessness (CICH) and Ending Chronic Homelessness through Employment and Housing—and the existing HUD-VASH program demonstrated key collaboration practices identified in our October 2005 report, such as defining roles and responsibilities and leveraging resources. Under the CICH, HUD, HHS, and VA agreed on roles and responsibilities and leveraged resources by allotting 3-year grants from HHS and VA and up to 5-year grants from HUD to 11 communities.[42] Similarly, Ending Chronic Homelessness through Employment and Housing was a partnership between Labor and HUD in which, through a cooperative agreement, HUD and Labor defined roles and responsibilities and leveraged resources, also consistent with key collaboration practices.[43] Since 2008, under the HUD VASH program, HUD has designated more than 30,000 tenant-based Section 8 vouchers to public housing authorities for veterans who are homeless and VA provided funding for supportive services, including case management and clinical services.[44] Particularly, VA identified a number of Veterans Affairs Medical Centers to participate in the program and provide case management resources. While these efforts demonstrated practices that enhanced and sustained collaboration, particularly linking housing assistance and supportive services, HUD-VASH has not demonstrated collaborative strategies that could benefit rural areas specifically, according to officials and rural service providers in some of the states we visited. Because the HUD vouchers must be linked to VA facilities, the recipients of the vouchers have been mostly in nonrural areas in which most VA medical centers are located. However, according to HUD officials, innovative approaches, such as using a mobile clinic, are now being used to serve rural areas. Furthermore, according to VA officials, HUD and VA have discussed opportunities to improve voucher allocation in rural areas.[45]

Additionally, the Interagency Council has developed the first-ever Federal Strategic Plan to Prevent and End Homelessness. The plan, which was presented to Congress on June 22, 2010, reflects interagency agreements on a set of priorities and strategies agencies will pursue over 5 and 10-year timeframes according to population. Also, according to HUD and HHS officials, the two departments, as part of the President's fiscal year 2011 budget, are proposing two demonstration initiatives, one involving 4,000 housing vouchers with health, behavioral health, and other supportive services for chronically homeless persons, and another involving 6,000 housing vouchers linked with mainstream services like job training and income assistance through TANF for homeless and at-risk families with children. Additionally, according to HUD and HHS officials, the two departments established working groups to identify collaboration opportunities related to homelessness. However, given that the Council's strategic plan has only recently been released and that the proposal in the President's fiscal year 2011 budget has yet to be approved, the impact of both of these efforts is uncertain.

According to officials and providers we interviewed, HUD and HHS are the key agencies serving the general population of those experiencing homeless. For instance, HUD officials noted that the agency was the only federal provider of permanent supportive housing for the homeless. While several agencies provide supportive services, including HUD, the health-related services on which HHS focuses correspond to needs often associated with persons experiencing homelessness, particularly mental health and substance abuse treatment (see table 5).[46] Service providers with whom we spoke consistently cited HHS as the appropriate agency for supportive services.

Table 5. Examples of Supportive Services That Federal Agencies, Excluding HUD, Can Provide to Persons Experiencing Homelessness

		Subpopulation	
Types of supportive services	Adult or family	Youth	Veteran
Health services			
Case management	HHS	HHS	VA and HHS
Mental health	HHS	HHS	VA and HHS
Medical	HHS	HHS	VA and HHS
Substance abuse treatment	HHS	HHS	VA and HHS
Nonhealth services			
Education	-	Education	-
Food	DHS and USDA	DHS, HHS, and USDA	DHS and USDA
Job training	Labor and HHS	Labor	Labor and HHS

Source: GAO.

However, according to officials and rural providers we interviewed (and nonrural providers interviewed for our June 2010 report), there is little evidence that HUD and HHS have formally agreed on their respective roles and responsibilities, or identified ways to leverage resources to support the delivery of coordinated housing and supportive services.[47] According to HUD officials, beginning in 2002, in response to a requirement in the 2001 HUD Appropriations Act, HUD shifted its emphasis towards funding housing for persons experiencing homelessness.48 This reduced the proportion of the total CoC funding which went to supportive services from 50 percent in 2002 to 34 percent in 2008, as illustrated in figure 3. In subsequent years, CoCs submitted new and renewal projects with mostly housing activities (such as operation and leasing), and according to HUD officials, this resulted in more than 40,000 newly constructed housing units.49 During this shift towards housing assistance, HUD required new and renewal applicants to provide information on how those projects planned to coordinate and integrate with other mainstream health, social services, and employment programs. Even though HUD officials noted that it relied on other federal agencies to fill the supportive services gap, providers we visited told us they are challenged to secure supportive services funding from agencies other than HUD. A requirement that HUD applicants provide information on plans to coordinate with other agencies does not directly address this concern of these service providers.

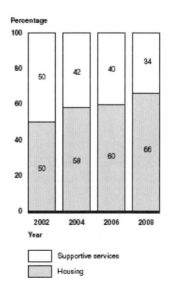

Source: HUD.

Figure 3. HUD's CoC Housing and Supportive Services Distribution.

HUD and HHS, which both have missions to address homelessness, have not adopted some of the key practices that could be used to enhance collaborative efforts, particularly during the period when HUD shifted its resources and responsibilities. HUD officials said that they consulted with HHS prior to their shift in resources and responsibilities. HHS officials told us that there was no formal discussion or agreement between them and HUD about how HHS might fill the gap in supportive services created by HUD's shift toward housing. We previously have recommended that federal agencies adopt a formal approach—including practices such as a memorandum of agreement or formal incentives focused on collaboration, signed by senior officials—to encourage further collaboration. However, while HUD and HHS have not previously done this, they reported that they have started discussions as part of their demonstration initiatives for fiscal year 2011.[50]

Without formally linking housing and supportive services across federal agencies, federal efforts to address homelessness may not be as effective as they could be. According to HUD officials, from 2001 to 2007, HUD and several partners—HHS, VA, Labor, Education, and the Interagency Council—held a series of Policy Academies which focused on fostering collaboration, enhancing partnerships, and building capacity. Additionally, HHS and HUD collaborated to create FirstStep to encourage use of mainstream services. However, the impact of this collaboration is not clear, as evidenced by numerous rural providers who were not aware of the collaboration. In addition, service providers with whom we spoke in both rural and nonrural areas consistently raised concerns about the lack of coordination between HUD and HHS. In spite of HUD's housing emphasis, which encouraged local communities to coordinate with other mainstream supportive services programs, and HUD's efforts in issuing guidance to rural areas on ways to collaborate with other organizations, some service providers we spoke with mentioned that they did not observe coordination across federal agencies.[51] They cited the administrative challenges they faced in developing programs for the homeless that incorporated both housing and services.[52] Particular to Kentucky, state officials and service providers told us that HHS's PATH program, due to state stipulations, limits resources for serving rural clients, many of whom suffer from mental health or substance abuse problems. The lack of service dollars also affects organizations that could access HHS funding. Officials who administer several shelter and transitional housing programs in rural Maine told us they sought nongovernmental funding to fill the gaps in services. For example, HHS's Transitional Living Program provided $200,000 for supportive services over 5 years, but the officials had to seek additional supportive services funds through foundations and private donors. Development by HUD and HHS of formal efforts to link housing and services, which may include their proposed collaboration in the President's fiscal year 2011 budget, could enhance the effectiveness of federal efforts to address homelessness.

CONCLUSION

The issue of rural homelessness presents a number of challenges for federal agencies, not the least of which is determining its extent. Data limitations and the array of federal programs, some of which are not specifically targeted toward homelessness and some of which do not track if their services or dollars have been expended in rural areas or on persons experiencing homelessness, have resulted in multiple data sets that do not allow for an overall assessment of the characteristics and extent of rural homelessness or a comparison with nonrural homelessness. The data issues are enormously challenging, but they also highlight the importance of coordinating within existing programs to mitigate some of the impact of the information gaps and to effectively deliver services.

As HUD and HHS consider collaborative efforts to address homelessness, formal coordination across these agencies that links supportive services and housing—a model that has shown to be effective—needs to include tangible and accessible opportunities for providers to bridge the gap in funding for supportive services that can be joined with housing for persons experiencing homelessness. Providers with whom we met in rural areas were generally unaware of any collaborative efforts between HUD and HHS that would assist them in linking housing and supportive services. Particularly during HUD's shift in its resources and responsibilities in 2002, HHS and HUD, the primary agencies for supportive services and housing, did not implement some of the key practices for effective collaboration that could have limited gaps in services. More effective collaboration can create incentives and opportunities for homeless housing and supportive services to be linked, which is considered to be important for the effective delivery of assistance to persons experiencing homelessness, and to further reduce administrative challenges for local service providers. By more formally linking housing and supportive services, HUD and HHS could increase their ability and opportunities to address gaps in efforts to effectively address homelessness and decrease challenges to service providers and persons experiencing homelessness.

RECOMMENDATION FOR EXECUTIVE ACTION

To strengthen formal collaboration efforts, we recommend that the Secretary of Housing and Urban Development and the Secretary of Health and Human Services direct the appropriate program offices to further explore opportunities to more formally link housing and supportive services—in the most appropriate forms and combinations of mainstream and targeted programs identified by both agencies—with specific consideration for how such collaboration could minimize barriers to service provision in rural areas.

AGENCY COMMENTS AND OUR EVALUATION

We provided draft copies of this report to the Departments of Agriculture, Education, Health and Human Services, Housing and Urban Development, Interior, Labor, and Veterans Affairs and the Executive Director of the US Interagency Council on Homelessness for their review and comment. Both HHS and HUD generally agreed with our recommendation and provided technical comments which we incorporated, as appropriate. The Departments of Labor and Veterans Affairs and the staff of the US Interagency Council on Homelessness did not provide formal comments but provided technical comments which we also incorporated, as appropriate. The Departments of Agriculture and Interior did not provide any comments.

HUD's Assistant Secretary of Community Planning and Development stated in written comments that HUD agrees that increased collaboration among federal agencies would improve the delivery of services in rural areas. In addition, HUD stated that due to statutory requirements, federal agencies do not employ a single definition of "rural" and it may not be reasonable for all agencies to utilize the same definition of rural as the purposes of the programs may be vastly different. We do not recommend that agencies utilize a single definition of rural but rather recognize that the varying definitions limit the ability to understand the incidence and prevalence of homelessness in rural areas. HUD also commented that this report presents a limited review of HUD's data collection and reporting efforts and does not acknowledge the progress that HUD has been making in this area or the value of the data currently being collected, or that their Annual Homeless Assessment Report is the only national estimate of homelessness to use longitudinal data. Since we recently issued a report that provides a detailed review of HUD's data collection and reporting efforts and discusses the efforts HUD has taken to improve the data, we did not provide this same level of detail in this report.[53] We have added a reference to our June 2010 report for additional information on these topics. In addition, as noted in our June 2010 report, HUD's data in their Annual Homeless Assessment Report are not longitudinal in that they do not follow specific individuals over time; rather HUD collects aggregated data that track numbers of homeless over time.

HUD commented that they have undertaken efforts to better align their homelessness data with homelessness data from HHS and VA. We acknowledged these efforts in the report. HUD also commented that the report indicates that effective collaboration hinges predominately on the use of a common vocabulary and offered barriers it considers more significant to effective collaboration. Discussions of issues related to a common vocabulary are not described in this report but are included in our June 2010 report.[54] Additionally, while HUD agrees with our discussion about the proportion of CoC dollars awarded for supportive services activities having decreased, they commented that the total dollar amount associated with those service remains significant. We do not suggest that the total dollar amount of HUD funded supportive services is insignificant, but rather that the decrease in the proportion of dollars for supportive services has contributed to a gap in funding for providers. Further, HUD commented that it has worked with HHS to improve access by homeless persons to their programs and that federal coordination and collaboration are evident in the US Interagency Council on Homelessness's *Federal Strategic Plan to Prevent and End Homelessness*. We recognize in our report actions that HUD and HHS have taken to collaborate; however, we believe that we correctly assess the opportunities for further progress by the agencies in linking housing and supportive services across their programs.

HUD also commented that it agreed that a common vocabulary among federal agencies and increased collaboration would improve the delivery of services in rural areas, but that the existence of both of these elements does not equate to a seamless integration of various streams of funding to create a project to serve homeless persons. We are not suggesting that a common vocabulary and increased collaboration by themselves will equate to a seamless integration of funding streams, but we believe that it could help to improve the delivery of services. Finally, HUD commented that it believes our report's focus on the anecdotal experiences of local providers does not provide a complete picture of efforts made by HUD regarding data collection, interagency collaboration, and the funding of supportive services. As noted earlier, we did not seek to repeat the level of detail on HUD's efforts regarding data collection as had already been included in our June 2010 report and we refer readers to this report for additional information.[55] Also, while our report provides the perspectives of local providers as gathered from six site visits, we also conducted numerous interviews with national stakeholder groups and federal agency officials, and reviewed relevant reports and federal agency documents. Based on all of the information we gathered and reviewed, we believe we have correctly assessed the data collection, interagency collaboration, and funding of supportive service issues referred to by HUD in their comment.

HHS's Deputy Assistant Secretary for Legislation stated in written comments that HHS strongly agrees with the importance of collaboration with HUD to effectively address homelessness. In addition, HHS commented that GAO's reference to the demonstration initiative—around housing vouchers for homeless people—included in the Fiscal Year 2011 President's Budget was incomplete. We added an expanded description of this initiative. HHS commented that the Patient Protection and Affordable Care Act will contribute to filling gaps in supportive services for homeless people. We did not examine the Patient Protection and Affordable Care Act as part of our review. HHS also commented that the discussion of funding and services in the report needs to distinguish between linking homeless individuals with the services that they need and aligning services with housing programs that target specific homeless populations. We acknowledge that collaboration between HHS and HUD related to housing and supportive services could take different forms. As we state in our recommendation, the two agencies should explore opportunities to link housing and supportive services while considering the most appropriate forms and combinations for this collaboration.

List of Committees

The Honorable Christopher J. Dodd
Chairman

The Honorable Richard C. Shelby
Ranking Member
Committee on Banking, Housing, and Urban Affairs
United States Senate

The Honorable Robert Menendez
Chairman

The Honorable David Vitter
Ranking Member
Subcommittee on Housing, Transportation and
Community Development Committee on Banking, Housing, and Urban
Affairs
United States Senate

The Honorable Barney Frank
Chairman

The Honorable Spencer Bachus
Ranking Member
Committee on Financial Services
House of Representatives

The Honorable Maxine Waters
Chairwoman

The Honorable Shelley Moore Capito
Ranking Member
Subcommittee on Housing and Community Opportunity
Committee on Financial Services
House of Representatives

APPENDIX I. SCOPE AND METHODOLOGY

To address all of our objectives, we conducted site visits to six states—
Arizona, Kentucky, Maine, Minnesota, New Mexico, and Texas. During these
visits, we interviewed federal, state, and local housing and homelessness
officials and nonprofit homelessness organizations, and toured rural areas in
which homelessness was present. We selected the site visit locations based on
several factors, including (1) discussions with advocates and researchers in the
field of homelessness—including the Housing Assistance Council, the
National Alliance to End Homelessness, the National Law Center on
Homelessness and Poverty, and the Urban Institute—to learn about rural

homelessness issues and the outcomes across different states; (2) a review of studies and reports on local and state efforts to serve the homeless in rural areas, including papers prepared for the 2007 National Symposium on Homelessness Research that highlighted issues related to rural homelessness; (3) the presence of tribal lands and colonias; and (4) geographical diversity. While on site visits we interviewed federal field office officials, state officials, local providers, and local advocates, and in Minnesota panels of homeless individuals. We also toured service areas and providers facilities, and in Texas we toured several colonias. On the site visits to Arizona and New Mexico we visited the tribal lands of the San Carlos Apache Tribe of the San Carlos Reservation, Arizona; the Tohono O'odham Nation of Arizona; the Pueblo of Acoma, New Mexico; and the Pueblo of San Felipe, New Mexico. We interviewed tribal officials from the tribal designated housing entities, service providers on and off tribal lands, and advocates. We reviewed relevant laws, regulations, and program documentation and interviewed officials from various federal agencies, including Departments of Agriculture, Education, Health and Human Services, Housing and Urban Development, Interior, Labor, Veterans Affairs, and the US Interagency Council on Homelessness (Interagency Council). We also conducted interviews with a variety of stakeholders, including advocates and researchers.

To describe the characteristics of homelessness in rural areas, we reviewed existing research and studies on homelessness issues, particularly those that are related to rural homelessness. We conducted interviews with relevant federal and state officials, service providers, national homeless and poverty organizations, and to the extent possible, homeless individuals and families to obtain their perspectives on the conditions of homeless in rural areas and the extent of migration to nonrural areas for assistance. Specifically, we interviewed federal officials to understand the extent data is available in estimating the incidence and prevalence of homelessness in rural areas and how it compares to nonrural areas.

To identify the federal homeless assistance and amount of funding awarded, we reviewed statutes, regulations, and reports, including our prior work, on federal homeless assistance for both targeted and mainstream programs. We interviewed federal, state, and local officials, to understand the range of assistance that is available to assist homeless individuals or families in rural areas, how those assistance programs are delivered, and the amount of funding that has been awarded. To the extent that data were available for comparison, we interviewed selected federal officials to understand funding differences between rural and nonrural areas. Specific data from some programs funded by the Departments of Agriculture, Housing and Urban Development, and Veterans Affairs were determined to be reliable enough to use in this report.

To identify the barriers persons experiencing homelessness and homeless service providers encounter, we interviewed state and local officials, homeless service providers, and to the extent possible, homeless individuals and families for information on barriers encountered when seeking assistance, barriers encountered when providing assistance, and any challenges related to federal coordination and efforts. We also interviewed select federal officials, including officials from the Interagency Council, to understand the extent of federal collaboration in providing services to persons or families experiencing homelessness in rural areas.

We conducted this performance audit from September 2009 to July 2010 in accordance with generally accepted government auditing standards. Those standards require that we plan and perform the audit to obtain sufficient, appropriate evidence to provide a reasonable basis for our findings and conclusions based on our audit objectives. We believe that the evidence obtained provides a reasonable basis for our findings and conclusions based on our audit objectives.

End Notes

[1] K. Hopper and J.Hamburg, "The Making of America's Homeless: From Skid Row to New Poor, 1945–1984," Critical Perspectives on Housing, R. G. Bratt, C. Hartman, and A. Myerson (Eds.), (Philadelphia, PA., Temple University Press 1986).

[2] The HEARTH Act is contained in Division B of Public Law 111-22. Pub. L. No. 111-22 § 1001, et seq., 123 Stat. 1669 (May 20, 2009). The Rural Stability Housing Grant Program was established in section 1401 of the HEARTH Act. The pertinent provisions of the act become applicable on November 20, 2010, or 3 months after the Department of Housing and Urban Development's (HUD) publication of final regulations under section 1504 of the act, whichever is earlier. The act requires HUD to promulgate the regulations not later than 1 year after the date of enactment. Id. §§ 1503, 1504.

[3] Id. § 1402. Colonia, a Spanish word for neighborhood or community, refers to a settlement located within 150 miles of the US-Mexico border that has a majority population composed of individuals and families of low and very low income and which may lack basic infrastructure such as water and sewer.

[4] The HEARTH Act changed various aspects of the Emergency Shelter Grant program and also changed the name of the program to the Emergency Solutions Grant program. Pub. L. No. 111-22 § 1201.

[5] The act was originally named the Stewart B. McKinney Homeless Assistance Act, Pub. L. No. 100-77 (July 22, 1987), but was renamed as the McKinney-Vento Homeless Assistance Act in 2000, Pub. L. No. 106-400 (Oct. 30, 2000).

[6] The HEARTH Act codified the CoC process. Pub. L. No. 111-22 § 1301. Among other things, the act requires a collaborative application for each geographic area applying for HUD McKinney-Vento funds.

[7] In this report we use "supportive services" to include all nonhousing services that may assist persons experiencing homelessness.

[8] The Interagency Council members are HUD; HHS; Education; Labor; DOJ; VA; DHS; the Departments of Agriculture, Commerce, Defense, Interior, Energy, and Transportation; the Social Security Administration; the General Services Administration; the Office of Management and Budget; the Postal Service; the Corporation for National and Community Service; and the White House Office of Faith-Based and Neighborhood Partnerships.

[9] Pub. L. No. 111-22 § 1004.

[10] GAO, Homelessness: A Common Vocabulary Could Help Agencies Collaborate and Collect More Consistent Data, GAO-10-702 (Washington, D.C.: June 30, 2010).

[11] Two of HUD's programs, the Emergency Shelter Grant program and the Homeless Prevention and Rapid Rehousing program, may fund homelessness prevention.

[12] The definition of "homeless children and youths" is codified at 42 USC. § 11434a.

[13] In April 2010 HUD published a proposed rule designed to clarify and elaborate the definitions of "homeless," "homeless individuals," "homeless person," and "homeless individual with a disability." Comments were due on June 21, 2010. 75 Fed. Reg. 20541 (Apr. 20, 2010).

[14] GAO, Rural Housing: Changing the Definition of Rural Could Improve Eligibility Determinations, GAO-05-110 (Washington, D.C.: Dec. 3, 2004).

[15] Cranston-Gonzalez National Affordable Housing Act, Pub. L. No. 101-625 (Nov. 28, 1990).

[16] Tribal officials defined a unit as overcrowded if there were more than one-and-a-half people per bedroom. Some units had three or more people per bedroom.

[17] GAO-10-702.

[18] HUD developed the data standards pursuant to the 2001 amendments to the McKinney-Vento Act. For a discussion of the Congressional directive, see HUD, Report to Congress: HUD's Strategy for Homeless Data Collection, Analysis and Reporting, Congressional Directive/HUD Study, (August 2001), http://www.hud.gov/offices/cpd/homeless/ hmis/ strategy/.

[19] PIT counts are conducted biennially, but HUD has compiled national data on homelessness for AHAR in each of the last 5 years (2005-2009). In the odd numbered years, the PIT was required for all CoCs and in 2006 and 2008 it was optional. The most recent PIT count was conducted in January 2010. The last AHAR was issued in June 2010 and includes data collected in January 2009.

[20] According to HHS officials, organizations that receive PATH funds are required to submit an annual PATH Report, providing information about funding, staffing, enrollment, services, and demographics of recipients. Similarly, health centers that receive specific funding as part of the Health Care for the Homeless Program are required to track information including patient demographics, services provided, staffing, clinical indicators, utilization rates, costs, and revenues.

[21] According to VA officials, VA staff, working with community providers in local meetings and planning processes, collect population based data on homeless veterans and conduct assessments of local service needs. For more information on statutory requirements, see Public Laws 102-405, 103-446, and 105-114.

[22] For additional information on actions HUD has taken to improve the data, see GAO-10-702.

[23] GAO, Homelessness: Information on Administrative Costs for HUD's Emergency Shelter Grants Program, GAO-10-491 (Washington, D.C.: May 20, 2010).

[24] ESG has been funded at approximately $160 million per year for several years.

[25] Eligibility requirements for entitlement cities or counties were established in section 102 of the Housing and Community Development Act and include central cities of metropolitan areas, other cities with a current population of 50,000 or more that are also in metropolitan areas, counties that are in metropolitan areas and which have a population of 200,000 or more after excluding metropolitan cities, small cities that do not participate with the county, and eligible tribes and cities or counties that retain status as a result of previously meeting the relevant criteria. The ESG funds are allocated in a three step process: First, 2 percent of the funds are set aside for the territories. Second, the balance of the funds is allocated by the CDBG formula. Third, as required by law, funds for entitlement jurisdictions that would receive less than 0.05 percent of the overall allocation—$80,000 in 2009—are added to the allocation of the state in which the jurisdiction is located. In 2009, 304 entitlement jurisdictions received a separate allocation, while 48 percent of ESG funding was distributed by state entities.

[26] CoCs submit a single application that includes a ranked list of individual organization projects and a comprehensive CoC wide planning document that outlines the activities, planning process, and needs assessment of the CoC. HUD scores the application as a whole but funds the projects directly.

[27] HUD determines a final pro rata need each year for each CoC utilizing the CDBG formula, the ESG Program's universe of jurisdictions, and the funding needed to renew all expiring Supportive Housing programs for one year. Using the CDBG formula, 75 percent of the funds are allocated to metropolitan cities and urban counties who have qualified for a direct ESG allocation since 2004 and the remaining 25 percent of the funds are allocated to all other metropolitan cities or urban counties and all other counties. A CoC's total preliminary pro rata need is the sum of the funds allocated to each municipality or county that participates in the CoC. A CoC's final pro rata need may be adjusted up if the funding required to renew its expiring Supportive Housing projects exceeds its preliminary pro rata need.

[28] Since 1997, New Mexico, Arizona, and Texas have set aside 10 percent of their CDBG funds for the colonias and California has set aside from 2 to 5 percent.

[29] Congressional Research Service, Homelessness: Targeted Federal Programs and Recent Legislation, RL30442 (Washington, D.C., Jan. 20, 2010).

[30] Labor uses "nonurban" rather than rural in its Homeless Veterans' Reintegration program. Labor chose 569,463 to include the largest 75 cities in its urban category. All other areas below that population number, regardless of size, are eligible for competition in the nonurban category.

[31] According to the National Alliance to End Homelessness, a 2007 report noted that between 1997 and 2007, 170,000 public units and 300,000 federally subsidized private market units have been lost due to deterioration.

[32] The Low-Income Housing Tax Credit program provides an indirect federal subsidy used to finance the development of affordable rental housing for low-income households.

[33] Tenant-based Section 8 vouchers assist very low-income families, the elderly, and the disabled with affordable, decent, safe, and sanitary housing in the private market. Tenant-based Section 8 vouchers are administered locally by public housing agencies (PHAs). The PHAs receive federal funds from HUD to administer the voucher program. A family that is issued a housing voucher is responsible for finding a suitable housing unit that must meet minimum standards determined by the PHA.

[34] M.R. Burt, et. al., Homelessness: Programs and the People They Serve, Findings of the National Survey of Homeless Assistance Providers and Clients (Washington, D.C., Urban Institute, 1999).

[35] According to VA officials, HUD-VASH allows some waivers for felons.

[36] GAO-10-702.

[37] HUD, Office of Policy Development and Research, US Housing Market Conditions (May 2010).

[38] State and local governments that receive an ESG allocation by formula establish the reimbursement rate for ESG-funded activities. In Maine, "bednight" refers to one bed in an emergency shelter occupied for one night by one individual. The initial bednight per diem calculation is based on an amount equal to 85 percent of the funds available for the calendar year, which will be divided by a number equal to the total number of bednights of all eligible emergency shelters during the previous calendar year.

[39] GAO, Results-Oriented Government: Practices That Can Help Enhance and Sustain Collaboration among Federal Agencies, GAO-06-15 (Washington, D.C.: Oct. 21, 2005).

[40] In particular, mental illness, alcohol abuse, and drug abuse decreased for participants in the study, which are among some of the most costly public health problems in the country.

[41] L. Sadowski, R. Kee, VanderWeele, et al, "Effect of a Housing and Case Management Program on Emergency Department Visits and Hospitalizations Among Chronically Ill Homeless Adults: A Randomized Trial," JAMA, vol. 30, no. 17, 1771-1778 (2009); and T.E. Martinez and M.R. Burt, "Impact of Permanent Supportive Housing on the Use of Acute Care Health Services by Homeless Adults," Psychiatric Services, vol. 57, no. 7, 992-999 (2006).

[42] HUD, HHS, and VA (with the coordination of the Interagency Council) provided housing and supportive services for individuals experiencing chronic homelessness in 11 communities through CICH. According to research studies in behavioral sciences, the CICH demonstration project had positive outcomes due to the combination of resources including federal funding and oversight, technical assistance, and opportunities for meetings with other CICH communities. For more information, see M. Kresky-Wolff, M.Larson, R. O'Brien, and S. McGraw, "Supportive Housing Approaches in the Collaborative Initiative to Help End Chronic Homelessness (CICH)," The Journal of Behavioral Health Services and Research, Vol. 37, No. 2 (2010).

[43] Labor and HUD offered permanent housing, supportive services, and employment assistance to people who were chronically homeless. Martha Burt's study of the demonstration project in Los Angeles, California, found that the project succeeded in its goal of moving chronically homeless clients into permanent supportive housing and helping them get and keep employment. Martha Burt, Urban Institute, Evaluation of LA's HOPE: Ending Chronic Homelessness through Employment and Housing Final Report (Washington, D.C., 2007).

[44] The 2008 Consolidated Appropriations Act, which authorizes a joint effort between HUD and VA to coordinate housing and supportive services for homeless veterans, articulated steps for identifying roles and responsibilities and a system of leveraging resources. See Pub. L. No. 110-161 (Dec. 26, 2007).

[45] Although HUD-VASH is not included in the fiscal year 2011 budget, HUD officials said that they expect it will be included in future budgets.

[46] According to HHS officials, ongoing funding for services in permanent supportive housing is frequently funded through contracts with local departments of health, mental health, behavioral health and social services using HHS block grant resources.

[47] GAO-10-702.

[48] The 2001 HUD Appropriations Act included the requirement that no less than 30 percent of HUD's total appropriation must go to permanent supportive housing.

[49] Beginning in 2002, HUD began scoring CoCs on housing emphasis, which is a calculation based on the relationship between funds requested for housing activities and funds requested for supportive service activities. Furthermore, HUD began scoring CoCs on enrollment and participation in various mainstream programs.

[50] GAO, Rural Economic Development: Collaboration between SBA and USDA Could be Improved, GAO-08-1123 (Washington, D.C.: Sep. 18, 2009).

[51] For HUD's guidance to rural communities see HUD, Homeless Assistance Programs: Rural Continuum of Care (June 2009). Also, as discussed previously, the McKinney-Vento programs, through the CoC system, require local communities to assemble partners to develop a comprehensive plan for housing and supportive service, such as case management, treatment programs, and training programs, to address the needs of those who are experiencing homelessness.

[52] GAO-10-702 identified similar challenges in nonrural areas.

[53] GAO-10-702.

[54] GAO-10-702.

[55] GAO-10-702.

INDEX